BOTANY FOR THE GARDENER

By the same author

BIOLOGY FOR THE CITIZEN
ELEMENTARY ECOLOGY
INTRODUCTION TO BIOLOGY

BOTANY FOR
THE GARDENER

DOUGLAS REID

Sometime Senior Biology Master, Harrow School,
Fellow of the Royal Society of Edinburgh,
Associate (hon. causa) of the Linnean Society of London

TAPLINGER PUBLISHING COMPANY
NEW YORK

First Published in the United States in 1967 by
TAPLINGER PUBLISHING CO., INC.
29 East Tenth Street
New York, New York 10003

S B
454
.R4

Library of Congress Catalog Card Number 67-25578

Printed in Great Britain

PREFACE

IT SEEMS to me that a knowledge of botany should be based on living plants, and what better place to start than in a garden? Too often is botany taught as if it were an abstract subject, with some facile talk of phloem, xylem, tropisms, etc., then all is forgotten! Or a school garden is run on the usual lines of 'do this or that', but phloem, xylem and tropisms are never brought into it.

This is a pity, because not only is an understanding of the structure of plants and the functions of their parts a help in their successful growing, but it adds to the interest (or so I think) to see the plant as a living thing – the tiny seed turning its store of starch into sugar; cells growing, dividing and becoming specialised to do particular jobs; fluids travelling up and down their appointed paths in the stem; the leaf making its supply of sugar from carbon dioxide gas by a method not yet achieved by man; the elaborate process of seed production and, as summer ends, the total disintegration perhaps of all this wondrous mechanism, whose repeatability is, as it were, condensed in the dormant seed.

This book is an attempt to bring together the facts of botany at the Ordinary Level of the G.C.E. and the principles necessary for successful amateur gardening. Suggestions for practical work are appended to several of the chapters, consisting of simple and easily performed experiments which should enable the reader to demonstrate to himself some of these facts and principles.

5

CONTENTS

CONTENTS

1

THE SOIL: LIME AND ACIDITY

TO SOME PEOPLE, alas, soil is just dirt; to the scientist it is a highly complex, almost living substance; to the gardener it is the main medium of his success or failure.

It is unsatisfactory, however, to dismiss the subject in this superficial way, for soil is a complex substance and the more we know about it the better – where it comes from, of what it is composed, how its composition affects plants and how it can, if poor, be improved.

Soil has been defined as 'an aggregate of mineral particles containing humus', but that leaves a great deal unsaid. Mineral particles, for instance, may be the size of boulders or shingle or sand or silt, and it is manifest that the first two are far too big to concern us, though in the course of time they may be ground down by weather until they, too, enter into the constitution of the soil. Sand and silt concern us rather closely because each may form a soil (sandy soil and clay).

Soil is derived from the rocks which, in time, have been broken down into smaller particles by those natural agencies, frost and thaw, rain and wind. That, however, is not the whole story, because the soil of a district may not be composed of the rocks of that district; the glaciers of the Ice Age may have collected soil and carried it considerable distances before drop-

9

ping it. Rivers, too, carry the finer particles for great distances before their rate of travel slows down enough to allow the particles to drop and thus form the alluvium of valleys. So the soil of our country may be a thin smear of finer materials of local or distant origin overlying the native rock.

The size of the grains composing the soil is of considerable importance for the growth of plants, because this affects its water-holding capacity. Between the grains there are gaps through which water will travel. If the gaps are large, water will pass down easily but it will not pass *up*. It is only when the gaps are small, as in clay or loam, that the water travels up and it continues to do so as long as there is sufficient water low down and evaporation from the surface. This ability of narrow spaces to hold water is called capillarity.

Plants normally get their water-supply from this water reserve which accumulates low down in the soil and which is constantly

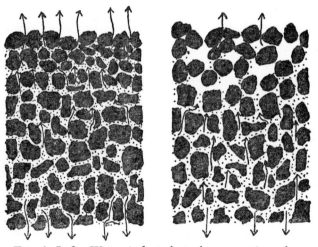

FIG. 1. Left: *Water is lost through evaporation when the soil surface is caked and the water-table falls rapidly.* Right: *When the surface is hoed, there is little evaporation so the water-table falls slowly.*

travelling up. But this reserve is not inexhaustible and as it travels up and evaporates from the surface so does the level of the reserve fall – just as the level of a pond falls due to evaporation in dry weather. It is possible, however, to retard the rate of evaporation of the water from the soil by keeping the surface loose, because in a loose surface the spaces are larger and the capillarity is in consequence reduced. Thus, less water is lost from a well-hoed bed than from one whose surface is caked.

This water-reserve (called the water-table) in the earth may be considered as an underground lake which, like any other lake, gets filled up by the winter rains. Over most of the country it is seldom or never visible, but in low-lying places it may reach the surface after very wet spells and will then cause marshy conditions.

The soil performs another mechanical function besides the holding of water – it holds the plants. If it is too loose water will not only fail to rise but seedlings may not get a proper grip, so, between the absence of water and their inability to fix themselves, their future is precarious.

The soil particles being composed of minerals, and those being chemical substances, they will provide food for the plants if they can be dissolved in the water surrounding both them and the plant roots. But it must not be concluded that *wet* soil is necessary for plant growth; indeed, almost the opposite is the case, and mere dampness is the ideal condition, except for plants adapted to live in bogs and marshes.

Roots as well as leaves must have air, and if the soil is waterlogged, then air will not be able to penetrate and the plants will ultimately die; therefore to overwater pot plants is to endanger their life. Swamp-living plants of the tropics whose roots are buried in hot mud, which is an utterly airless environment, get over the difficulty in breathing by sending up above the surface special roots whose function is to act as 'lungs'. Air, however, will penetrate quite easily into damp soil in temperate regions, so special breathing devices are not necessary. Surplus water must not, therefore, be allowed to lie about; if there is a tendency for this to happen drainage must be resorted to. Stones scattered through the soil help considerably in its effective drainage and though they may be annoying when making a fine seed bed, their advantages greatly outweigh their disadvantages. Fig. 2 illustrates simple forms of drains.

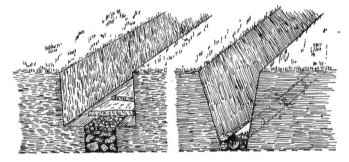

FIG. 2. *Simple drains*. Left: *Stones (or brushwood) with turves laid on top*. Right: *Tiles overlaid with stones or clinkers. These should slope down to a main drain or tank*.

Soil in which there is no free circulation of air tends to become acid (there are other causes to be discussed later) and this condition is not conducive to the healthy growth of most garden plants. Such acidity can often be reduced by digging the soil in the autumn and leaving it in as rough a condition as possible so that frost can penetrate and break it down.

Soil containing much lime (that is, soil on limestone or chalk, or that which contains a high proportion of sea-sand) presents a different problem. Water dissolves the lime and becomes loaded with calcium and this tends to act as a 'stopper' to the entry of adequate quantities of other substances into the plants. In consequence, some plants (for example, rhododendrons and other peat-lovers) fail to grow while others just fail to thrive. Where lime is very abundant, plants suitable for it should be chosen, and there are plenty of them.

But we may, oddly enough, find the soil on top of limestone or chalk to be quite acid, and this may be due to great quantities of manure having been dug into the soil for a long time, while the rain has washed the lime out of the cultivated layer.

The mention of manure brings us back to the other constituent of soil – humus. Humus is decaying organic matter, usually plant remains, without which a mass of mineral particles is not soil.

The humus performs four main functions. As it decays and breaks down, the substances of which it is composed become dissolved in the soil-water and are taken up by the plant roots; it helps to stop the soil from drying out in hot weather; it is a bad conductor of heat and so does not let the heat out (or the cold penetrate) in frosty weather; and it provides food for a great population of small plants (bacteria and moulds) and animals (worms and insect larvae) which have each their place in the economy of a well-balanced soil.

It is of the first importance, then, to see that the soil contains plenty of humus by adding organic matter to it. Just think what happens in an ordinary vegetable garden – seeds are sown, they grow into large plants by taking a great deal out of the soil; the cabbages are cut when wanted and later their stalks are pulled up and probably burnt; turnips, carrots, and so on are likewise removed and they all represent 'goodness' taken away.

If you keep on doing that year after year it is obvious that the soil will get poorer, and so must the cabbages, turnips and carrots. Therefore what you take out must be put back, so throw away no unwanted vegetable matter; make a heap of your garden waste, the weeds you pull up, grass-clippings, and potato peelings, and anything else of a like nature and let it rot (compost it, in other words), then in due course dig it back in. Even by this method there may be a loss, for you have eaten a lot of what the soil produced, so a supply from another source should be added if possible, that is by buying a load of farmyard manure. However this subject will be discussed in Chapter 3.

The cycle of nature – turning the land, sowing, hoeing, growth and mowing – is a slow and stately progression. We achieve little by trying to hurry it and we certainly get sounder, if not always such spectacular, crops if we do not.

It is usually assumed that the gardener's function is always to grow plants in his land, while it is forgotten that to be really successful he must succeed in *not* growing plants in one part of his garden, and the latter job is often harder than the former! I refer to the garden paths. Not to grow plants means that soil is not wanted, so barren cinders are laid down and compacted (concrete, of course, solves all difficulties at greater expense and much labour but the result is not pleasing), and it must be kept compacted because, do what you like, some soil from boots and implements will arrive on the path and seed will land on it and germinate, pushing delicate but determined roots into the mass. But the less that gets into the mass the better, so do not hoe the surface; pull out the weed when it is small or burn it off, for by hoeing you slowly but surely mix soil with the cinders and in time turn it all into soil.

Lime and Acidity

Now a little more must be said about lime. The continued use of natural manure tends in time to load the soil with the acids liberated in its disintegration (the so-called humic acids). Sooner or later an accumulation of humic acid could make the soil unsuitable for some forms of plant growth and also encourage the growth of organisms which will attack crops. The parasite (*Plasmodium*) which causes 'finger and toe' in turnips and club-root in cabbages flourishes in such conditions. A good dressing of an alkaline substance (lime, ground limestone or chalk) will counteract this and bring the soil back to a 'sweet' condition.

Diseases like those mentioned above are good indicators of acid conditions, but it is a little disheartening to have to wait till the crop is spoilt in order to know when to use lime. A far better method is to buy from any chemist some soil indicator at the cost of a few shillings and test the soil periodically. Full instructions for use are invariably given with the indicator.

Lime also, by neutralizing the acids in the manure and other organic matter in the soil, allows the bacteria to break it down sooner so that the food substances in it become more quickly available to the plants. By looking at a deposit of peat we can see at once what happens if a great deal of organic matter is allowed to accumulate year after year. A little decay takes place, acids are set free which stop further decay (bacterial action) and so the plant and animal remains in the peat become preserved and will so remain for ever – as far as we know. Only recently the body of a man was dug out of the peat in Denmark where it had been for a couple of thousand years; it was perfectly preserved, even to the contents of the stomach, which showed that he had been eating the seeds of various grasses! Indeed, much of our knowledge of the past has been gained from the study of peat.

Since manure is not put into the soil in order that it may be preserved for ever, we may as well see that there is enough lime present to help in its being broken down and given to the plants.

Those jobs performed by lime can be called its chemical function, but in certain soils it can perform a physical or mechanical function, too, and this is especially important in clay soils.

Clay is different from other soils in that the very fine particles of which it is composed will stick together when wet and if much trampled will form such a solid mass that water cannot pass through it at all. In this condition it is useless as a soil, though it may be excellent for making bricks. The addition of lime causes the fine particles to group together in little knots, leaving spaces between so that it now behaves towards water as if each of the knots of particles was a more or less solid grain, allowing water and air to pass more freely through the mass.

For general purposes a neutral (neither acid nor alkaline) or a slightly acid soil should be aimed at. Fig 3. shows the effects of unsatisfactory soils on carrots.

It is a wanton extravagance to use lime in conjunction with most artificial manures. These are already soluble in water, so do not have to be broken down by bacteria.

Besides testing the soil for acidity it is sometimes advisable, especially if some plants persistently show a tendency not to do well, to have the soil close to such plants analysed in case it may be short of some particular constituent. Advice about this can be obtained through the local council or agricultural college.

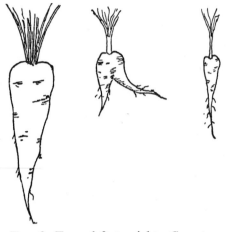

FIG. 3. From left to right: *Carrots grown in good loam; too rich a soil – unlimed clay; and in unenriched sand.*

My soil suffered for a long time with what looked like a deficiency in magnesium. This chemical is necessary although in quite minute quantities to make chlorophyll (the green colouring matter) in leaves. The leaves of many of the plants growing in the land in question varied from exceedingly pale green to almost white. Now what was odd was that the land is close to the sea and is almost constantly swept by winds carrying sea-salt and this should contain enough magnesium to supply the wants of all the plants in the district. To see if magnesium was deficient some of the plants in question were deliberately given magnesium, but without effect. A sample of the soil was then analysed and it was found to contain a very high proportion of calcium (being an old sea beach apparently) and this was in such quantities as to block the entrance of the magnesium into the plant roots. Well, it is easier to add something to the soil than to take something out of it and there being no easy way of neutralising the excess calcium one had simply to put up with it and not try to grow plants intolerant of it.

The main elements which must be in the soil for plant growth are nitrogen, phosphorus, potassium, magnesium and sulphur, and these will be present in compost or farmyard manure. If there is a gross deficiency of any particular one it may be made up by use of some special substance. Thus sulphate of ammonia will supply nitrate and sulphate; superphosphate, bone-meal and basic slag will supply phosphate; wood-ash and kainite will supply potash.

Though those few are the main constituents used in plant tissues they are by no means the only ones. Others occur in small quantities but are just as necessary for healthy growth, and are known as 'trace elements' because only a minute quantity is necessary – but necessary it is. The list of such necessary trace elements is constantly being increased (cobalt, sulphur, boron, manganese and so on) until one feels that soon it will be shown that some amount, however small, of *all* the chemical elements is necessary for really healthy plant growth.

In some cases the absence of a trace element does not show in the plant itself, but it may show very clearly in the animal which feeds on the plant. Herbivorous animals, such as sheep, confined to a particular district in which there is a shortage of cobalt, very soon register that shortage although the grass they are eating may look all right. The deficiency in this sheep is indicated by stoppage of growth, increasing feebleness, loss of wool and, finally death. If such ailing animals be dosed with cobalt they begin to recover almost at once; if the land is then given a supply of cobalt the deficiency in the sheep no longer occurs.

The absence of cobalt in garden vegetables is hardly likely to affect us human beings who eat them since we are omnivorous and will get all the cobalt we need from other sources; and this statement also applies, of course, to the other trace elements

2

THE FUNCTIONS OF WATER

HAVING ALREADY MENTIONED water several times in connection with the plant and the soil, now let us consider its functions in more detail.

The soil substances, mainly mineral salts, which the plant needs for part of its food (the other part is carbon-dioxide gas and will be dealt with later) must be dissolved in water before they can be absorbed by the roots. The mechanism by which these substances pass from the soil solution into the root cells is not fully understood by scientists, but once inside they pass, again in solution, up the vessels of the root and stem until they reach the leaves where they are to be used.

Water itself is taken into the root by a quite different mechanism known as osmosis. If a strong salt solution is separated from a weak one by a special kind of membrane known as a semi-permeable membrane, water tends to pass through the membrane from the weak solution into the strong. The walls of plant (and animal) cells can act as semi-permeable membranes and because cells contain comparatively strong solutions of salts, water moves into the root cells from the weak soil solution. If, however, strong solutions of fertilizers, which are usually made up from various salts, come into contact with cell walls, water tends to pass *from* the cells into the stronger fertilizer solution

18

outside, and damage or even death of the cells results. Such damage is called plasmolysis and can happen, for example, when the gardener is applying fertilizer to the soil surface; if through carelessness particles of fertilizer are allowed to fall on to the foliage instead of on to the soil, the first shower of rain will turn them into drops of very strong solution, the surface cells of the leaves will be plasmolyzed and killed and the leaf will appear scorched.

Water, then, is needed by the plant for the process of taking up and transporting its mineral foods, but it also performs another essential function. It is quite obvious that plants, with the exception of the woody parts of shrubs and trees, have little structural rigidity. They can be cut and broken easily, and yet they stand up against gravity and wind quite successfully; delicate leaves and petals retain their shape and position – but only so long as they have an adequate water supply. This is because of the phenomenon known as turgidity. Each cell may be thought of as a tiny balloon containing water instead of air. So long as it is blown up with water, it will retain its shape and remain quite rigid, but if it contains only a little water it will flop and become soft and flabby.

The wilting of a plant is due to the reduction of this water support or turgidity, and can happen under two main circumstances, namely, when there is insufficient available water in the soil, and when water is being removed from the foliage faster than the roots can supply it. Each of these circumstances requires some elaboration.

Under certain conditions soil may contain an appreciable quantity of water, and yet this water cannot be taken up by plants. It will be realized from what was said above concerning osmosis that if the water is saline, as in a salt marsh, osmosis will prevent roots from absorbing water, and if normal plants are placed in a salt marsh, they will die. A few highly specialized plants are able to take up water from brackish pools and these form the peculiar flora typical of our estuaries.

But plants also face another difficulty in obtaining water from the soil. The water is held by the forces of surface tension in a thin layer surrounding each of the soil particles and these forces must be overcome before the water can pass into the cells. As water enters the roots, the layer remaining round each particle of soil gets thinner and the surface tension holding it there increases until the plant can no longer overcome this force; water then ceases to pass into the roots, and the plant wilts. Soil in this condition is said to be at wilting point, and it is a remarkable fact that for a particular soil the wilting point is the same for all ordinary plants.

At the other end of the scale, after a soil has been completely saturated some of the water tends to be drained out by the pull of gravity but there comes a time when the surface tension forces

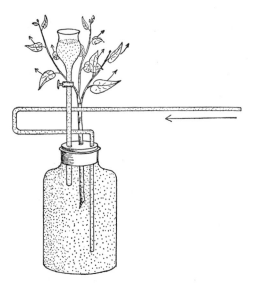

Fig. 4. *Measuring evaporation rate with a potometer. As water passes out of the leaves, so it runs back in the tube*

holding the water *in* are balanced by those of gravity tending to drain it *out*, so that though the soil is quite wet, no more drainage occurs. Such a soil is said to be at field capacity, holding its maximum possible amount of water against free drainage; in this condition the water it contains can very readily be taken up by roots.

The water represented by the difference between the amount in the soil at field capacity, and that in the same soil at wilting point is called the available water. This is the quantity of water which the plants can use. Different soils hold different amounts of water at field capacity and at wilting point and therefore contain different amounts of available water. Clay soils contain much available water; light sandy soils contain but little. Thus sandy soils need watering more often than heavy soils.

It was mentioned above that water might be removed from the foliage faster than the roots could supply it. The leaves to which the stem vessels bring the water have spaces inside them which communicate with the outside air by means of tiny pores called stomata. Energy from the sun evaporates water from the moist surfaces of the cells within the leaf into the spaces, and the vapour passes out of the stomata into the outside air. The warmer and drier the air, the faster is this evaporation, or transpiration as it is called; if there is a wind, the transpiration is faster still, because the dampened air is continually being replaced by drier air. This process goes on throughout the hours of daylight, even in cloudy weather. The cells which have had water taken from them obtain replacements from further down the plant and so a continuous upward movement of water takes place – the transpiration stream. Transpiration does not happen at night because, with the sun below the horizon, no energy is received from it. On a hot sunny day whole fields of large-leaved plants, such as cauliflowers or sugar beet, or plants in pots in a greenhouse, may wilt even though the soil may be quite wet. This so-called temporary wilting happens because the sun is sucking water out of the leaves faster than the roots can obtain it by osmosis from the soil.

It is important to realize that the whole process of transpiration is passive – that is the water is being drawn out of the plants by the sun – the plants are not, as used to be thought, pumping water out by their own efforts. It follows that to reduce transpiration one must shade the plants, reduce the temperature, moisten the air, and provide shelter from wind. Such treatment can restore a plant which has wilted temporarily in spite of its roots being in wet soil.

When there is a shortage of water within the leaf the stomata close and this to some extent reduces the amount of water being lost, but such stomatal closure can have a most undesirable secondary effect. Plants which are not provided with sufficient water to maintain adequate transpiration do not grow. The explanation is extremely simple. For their growth plants require not only the minerals which they obtain from the soil but also carbon-dioxide from the air and this they convert into sugars. This carbon-dioxide enters the leaves through the stomata and it cannot do this if water shortage has caused the stomata to close.

It will be as well at this point to correct a common fallacy concerning dew. The dew which condenses on the leaves of plants and on other cold surfaces during the early hours of the morning has indeed come from the air, but the air has obtained it as a result of evaporation from the soil surface below the plants. Thus dew is *not* a direct water gain to the plants. The leaves absorb some of the deposited water but the remainder is evaporated into the atmosphere and so the net result is a loss of soil water. However, many gardeners will testify that dew does seem to confer some benefit to plants possibly because the presence of water on the leaves reduces transpiration and so keeps up the supply of water within the plants; an alternative explanation is that perhaps the conditions favourable to dew formation are also favourable to plant growth. This is but one of the many things about plants which we do not yet fully understand.

Mention has already been made of the effect of temperature on the rate of transpiration. Temperature also affects most other processes within the plant. Within reason, the higher the temperature the faster the leaves can manufacture sugars and so the faster the plant grows. Conversely low temperature slows down the growth processes. In winter-time many plants become quite dormant and do not begin to grow again until the soil and the air begin to warm up. The germination of seeds and the rooting of cuttings is markedly affected by temperature. Gardeners are familiar with the principle of obtaining early germination and speeding up growth by means of a hot bed made over a heap of manure the decaying of which produces heat. The same principle is used in propagating frames but here the heat is usually obtained from hot water, steam or electricity.

Heat and water can be conserved in the soil by spreading a layer of insulating material over the surface, that is, mulching. The mulch may be manure, compost, straw, waste vegetable material, plastic sheet, or a film of sprayed bitumen or rubber, or it may be a thin dry layer of the soil itself – a dust tilth. The growth of many crops can be improved by mulching, but the mulch also encourages the growth of weeds and it is necessary to deal with these either by means of suitable herbicides, by very shallow hoeing, or by using black plastic (to deprive the weeds of light) and growing the desired crop plants through holes in the mulch.

3

ROTATION – MANURES – HYDROPONICS

Rotation

IT HAS ALREADY been noted that all plants do not take from the soil the same quantity of any particular substance nor all of the substances in the soil. It is a wise economy, therefore, to make groups of plants follow each other round: heavily manured soil is necessary for potatoes and the cabbage group; it is not necessary for onions, carrots, and so on, so the land which was manured for the first group will grow the second without further manurial treatment. As a result of using this method, there will be a constant rotation of the crops over the garden.

It must not be concluded, however, that the same crops can never be grown in the same plot for two or three years running, for this in the main is not so except in a few cases. I have a neighbour, for instance, who has grown potatoes in the same plot, year after year, for 30 years and he still gets excellent crops. Peas, however, often fail if grown in the same place for two or three years in succession. This is not due to any deficiency in the soil but to some soil fungi which seem to accumulate around the peas and, when in great enough concentration, attack the young plants as they come through the soil. For safety, then, it is better to rotate your cropping as much as possible.

Manures

One gets very tired of the one-sided and somewhat distorted campaign against inorganic fertilizers which seem always to leave so much unsaid. Of course it is a bad thing to use only artificials, but on the other hand they can be a great help.

The advantage of natural or farmyard manure lies in the fact that when put into the soil it breaks down slowly and so acts physically to conserve the water and heat in the soil. Chemically, it is likely to supply all the ingredients necessary for the growth and well-being of plants since it is composed of plant remains. However, some soils may be deficient in this or that substance so it is possible that the manure may be so too. Manure (urine) also contains substances which encourage the growth of roots (indole acetic acid), and for this reason farmyard manure is superior to artificials or even compost.

Compost, being partly broken-down or rotted vegetation, has much the same merits but can possibly have greater shortages of one or other of the essential basic substances than farmyard manure. This is because the latter was made by cattle which ate more substances than the local grass.

Compost is made simply by building a heap of vegetable matter and allowing it to rot. This, however, can be a slow process because if grass cuttings, and so on, are used, silage will first be formed and this does not interest the gardener. To by-pass this stage it is necessary to encourage the bacteria to keep working, and the cheapest but most laborious way to do so is to turn the heap over a few times. But if a thin layer of lime is added to the heap as it is being built, at about every 9 in., turning is not necessary. A little farmyard manure mixed through the heap also helps rotting. It is, of course, also possible to buy activators, which are quickest of all.

Inorganic manures contain known food substances suitable for plants but they may not contain the small quantities of trace elements, for instance, so necessary for healthy plant-growth. They have little, if any, physical effect on the soil and if unintelligently used may ruin it. On the other hand they are fairly soluble in water and so are more quickly available to the plant, and good crops follow correct usage.

There is much overstatement on the subject of artificial manures, their use even being given as a reason for the presence of such pests as carrot fly, onion fly and so on. In 1956 I had, for the first time, such a plague of these that my carrots and onions were totally destroyed and yet they were fertilized with pure farmyard manure.

I am also fairly certain that, despite the fact that potatoes and vegetables are said to have a poorer taste if grown with the help of inorganics, few people who say so could really distinguish by taste potatoes grown in the different media.

However, compost can be made by any gardener and should be made by all for the purpose of maintaining the organic matter content of the soil and its crumb structure: also for the sake of his own pocket, for it is a lot cheaper than inorganics. Some farmyard manure should be added to it if it can be got for the sake of its greater richness and the root-stimulating substances in it.

A little artificial manure added as a top-dressing is a great help in giving the plants a good start.

Hydroponics

It is, of course, possible to grow plants without soil. This process has now become a commercial proposition as a result of experimental work carried out to find how the absence of certain food-substances affected plant growth. It was done by making a series of solutions each containing all the necessary ingredients but one.

As a result of much experimentation in this direction it is now possible to make up a solution in which plants will grow sufficiently well to compete with those grown in garden soil.

This type of gardening is best carried on under cover. It involves the use of a tank – this may be filled with sand or burnt shale – which gives the support necessary to keep the plants upright but which supplies no food material. Into the tank is pumped the nutrient solution; it is important that this is kept circulating, otherwise the roots will become short of air and die.

This is only one of the many methods. Another is to put the plants in a layer of peat or some other such substance, on a wire gauze above a tank of the nutrient solution so that their roots can pass down into it. If the solution is to remain in the tank, then it must be constantly stirred by a propeller driven by a small electric motor in order that adequate aeration is achieved.

The nutrient solution is usually made up of the following substances – calcium nitrate, potassium dihydrogen phosphate, potassium nitrate, ferric tartrate, ammonium sulphate and magnesium sulphate in very dilute solution.

It is obvious that this soilless gardening has certain advantages over the more conventional type, for masses of soil and pots are not needed: there is no guesswork about what food supply the plants are getting, and there is no trouble from soil parasites, but experience has shown that a good knowledge of chemistry is needed if the correct balance of nutrients in the solution is to be maintained.

4

THE ORGANISMS IN THE SOIL:
ANIMALS – FUNGI AND BACTERIA

THERE ARE SO MANY living creatures in a bucketful of healthy soil that it has encouraged people to say that soil must be considered as a living entity. Though this may be straining the meaning of the word living to some extent, it is certainly a forceful way of describing soil. The poorer the soil the fewer living organisms are found in it, as one can easily see by examining sand or peat.

The soil organisms belong to both the animal and plant kingdoms and in each of those groups we can make a superficial examination of them.

Animals

The largest animal most exclusively confined to the soil is the mole. It is specially adapted for a burrowing life since its front feet are broad, powerful and possess heavy claws. The palms are turned outwards and the fur stands vertically on the body so that it cannot be ruffled whichever way the mole travels. The eyes are tiny and the sight poor as might be expected of an animal which has little use for seeing.

The mole is a carnivore so does no direct damage to plants by feeding on them, but the tunnels and molehills it makes can certainly disturb plants to their detriment, leaving the roots in air instead of soil. It feeds on earthworms and in doing so is no help to the gardener, but as it also eats insect larvae, which themselves feed on plant roots, it performs a valuable service.

If moles become a serious pest they can be trapped, using the Duffus patent mole-trap which is much more efficient than the old fashioned scissor-type traps. Poisoning by strychnine-treated worms is also very effective, but strychnine is a deadly poison and only available under licence from the local Ministry of Agriculture, National Agricultural Advisory Service Pest Officer.

The best-known member of the soil fauna is, of course, the earthworm, whose numbers can be a measure of the soil's fertility – if there are few worms in a garden, it is an indication that something should be done; manure added or drainage looked to.

As soil cultivators, some species of earthworm are of great importance because as they burrow, they swallow soil for the food it contains and then eject what they cannot digest. The soil is thus constantly being turned over, and since the worms may go down 6 ft. they are doing really deep cultivation.

It has been estimated that on good grassland such as a lawn or golf course, earthworms will bring up at least a 1 in. layer of soil in 10 years, which represents a good many tons to the acre. Worm-casts tend to be chemically nearer neutral than the original soil no matter whether it is acid or alkaline.

Some species also pull down into their burrows dead leaves which greatly add to the humic content of the soil; and when it is realized that this may amount to 20 lb. to the square yard during the six months or so that worms are active, it is no mean addition to the soil's fertility.

If the earthworm population rises to such a height as to be a positive nuisance, the numbers can be reduced by watering the soil with a mixture of 1 oz. of potassium permanganate evenly dissolved in 1 gall. of water to the square yard. Lead arsenate is also extremely effective at a rate of 2 oz. to the square yard. Children and animals must be kept away from treated areas for at least six weeks after application, since it is a deadly poison.

There is no evidence that earthworms do any damage to living plants and, indeed, their most serious disadvantage, and that a little one, is the unsightliness of their casts on a lawn or the seemingly serious obstacles such casts are to golfers.

By constantly burrowing down through the soil, the earthworms form channels down which air and water can get to the roots of the plants, and though water is not so dependent for such channels for its passage downwards, air is, and thus the earthworm is performing a work of the utmost importance.

None of the other 'creepy-crawlies' in the soil is of such direct benefit to it. Indeed, most do a considerable amount of damage. I have in mind here such animals as the millipedes, such insect larvae as the wire-worm, leather-jacket and cockchafer grub.

The wire-worm is the larva of the click-beetle. The larva gets its name from its shape – long, thin and somewhat flattened and its rather hard covering which suggests a bit of wire. It lives in the soil for five or six years feeding on the roots of plants and doing much damage. It is not easily got rid of but crop-rotation and cultivation of the land when fallow help a lot. Seed dressing with gamma-BHC gives protection to developing seedlings.

The leather-jacket is the larva of the daddy-longlegs and is very unlike the foregoing because it is thick, tough-skinned and legless. It too feeds on plant roots and is difficult to eradicate though, besides cultivation and crop rotation, treatment with either DDT liquid or dust in mild humid weather during autumn or spring is effective.

The cockchafer is a large, night-flying beetle which lays its eggs in vegetation. The larva is often found when turning the garden soil. It is large, white and fleshy and is curved into a half circle. The head is brown. This larva does much damage to plant roots but it is easily seen and destroyed when digging the ground. Gamma-BHC and DDT are the best chemicals for controlling cockchafers.

It is, however, possible that general fumigation of the soil is the only answer if pests are abundant, but this is not always a cheap process. In the case of greenhouse soil it may be worth while to pipe steam into it, and so raise its temperature to a point at which the pests are killed; this is called partial soil sterilization.

Chemical substances worked into the soil are also effective. Formalin may be worked into the soil or carbon bisulphide may be injected into limited areas with a syringe.

There are two superficially similar animals which are apt to be confused, namely centipedes and millipedes, but their habits are so different that it is worth bothering to decide which is which. Both are long and thin with the body divided into segments all along its length. The centipede, however, is more flattened and has one pair of legs on each segment except the first few.

The habits are equally different, for the centipede is normally carnivorous and feeds on slugs, insects and insect larvae, so on the whole it is beneficial to the gardener. Not so is the millipede which eats rootlets, potatoes, turnips, etc. Its jaws, however, are rather weak so it has to confine its depredations to either soft tissues or those which have already been damaged by some other agency. Liming the soil seems to reduce their numbers and both Gamma-BHC and DDT can be used as control measures.

But such large animals do not constitute more than an infinitesimally small proportion of the fauna of the soil. Where a spadeful of earth may contain three earthworms and a cockchafer larva, it will also contain thousands of tiny, microscopic forms not visible to the naked eye. Those are the soil protozoa, each composed of a single cell – a mere dot of living matter – which, despite its smallness, is feeding, breathing, moving and reproducing just like the more visible forms.

All of those protozoa are living on organic matter; some few may attack the tissues of the living plant, but the great majority of them are busy breaking down the dead organic matter in the soil, the humus, and reducing it to a form in which its constituents are available to the plants.

At the present time, however, much work still remains to be

done on the relations between protozoa and the soil. It is known that their numbers fluctuate rapidly and to a great extent, and it has been suggested that when their numbers become, and stay, very high we get the condition known as 'soil-sickness'. This is, however, now considered to be caused by plant parasitic nematodes or eelworms. There are, however, many species of soil-living eelworms which do not attack plants.

Fungi and Bacteria

These plants will be discussed in greater detail in a later chapter, but a little may be said about them here. Considering the fungi as moulds, both they and the bacteria are abundant in soil. The moulds, however, prefer more acid soils containing plenty of organic matter in a little decayed state. They will not be present in great numbers in well-cared-for soil and their place will be taken by soil bacteria which do their work best in alkaline soil.

It follows from this that the organic matter put into the soil should be well rotted and that the acidity of the soil should be kept low by the addition of lime.

Some moulds, unfortunately, have a tendency to attack living plants and thus we get them attacking seedlings (damping-off), and the leaves of roses (mildew), strawberry fruits (grey mould) and a host of other plants. Many moulds, of course, are naturally beneficial.

From the foregoing it will be seen that there is something to be said for those who consider the soil to be almost a living entity: but even if we do not go as far as this, we must consider it as being packed with a mighty army of helpers (with some few hinderers, of course), and it is up to any sensible gardener to see that so many friends are well treated. So give them what keeps them happy – plenty of humus, enough lime to stop the soil going acid (unless you are growing rhododendrons or related plants) and plenty of air by keeping it open with spade and hoe. This is little enough recompense for all their work.

5

THE CELL – THE ROOT – THE SHOOT

The Cell

BEFORE DISCUSSING the structure and jobs done by the various more obvious parts of the plant-body, it is necessary to look for a little at what might be called the bricks with which it is built. Something of them can be seen quite clearly if a polished piece of wood, preferably in cross-section, be examined with even a simple magnifying glass. The little cavities, each surrounded by a thick wall, are all that remain of the once-living plant cells.

In the plant, when those cells were alive and before the thick woody walls were formed, each cell was a tiny closed box containing a quantity of a fluid somewhat like watery gelatine or gum, in the centre of which was a large space, the vacuole, containing a liquid known as the cell sap. The jelly-like fluid was the living matter of the plant, the protoplasm, little different from the protoplasm of which we are ourselves composed. It was differentiated, into the cytoplasm, the main body of the cell and the nucleus, whose function is to control the cell in such a venture as growth, for since one cell can arise only from another, growth cannot take place without cell-division.

It is from this uninteresting, greyish, semi-fluid that there stems all the wonderful activities of even the most gorgeous plants – the passage of fluids up and down the stem, the taking

C   33

in of some substances by the roots and the exclusion of others, the opening of the buds in spring, the often elaborate pollination mechanism of the flower and not only its colours but their arrangement.

It often strikes one when asked to admire some perfect bloom, that its perfect shape and colour is the least of its wonders. What of its elaboration from the earth's stores and the atmosphere's waste, the pulling down of the sun's energy to bind all these together, and the tireless fetching and carrying, sorting out and mixing done by that organism which never thought a thought, produced no audible poem and which the finest music passes by with less effect than a summer puff of wind? Where then, does the real beauty lie – on the culminating bloom or in all the unknown processes which went to make it? We admire, but do we stop to wonder?

The living protoplasm of the cell, then, is the unit of the plant and the number of cells in even a small plant is legion. The living contents of all these cells is more or less the same, but the shape of the cells differs very considerably and depends on what job the cell is doing. Some indication of the differences will appear as we discuss the parts of the plant.

Though a plant is usually considered as being composed of the root, shoot, leaf and flower, I propose to start the examination of the parts in the logical way, namely, as they appear from the germination of the seed.

The Root

When adequate warmth and moisture strike the ripe seed the young root pushes its way out and bends downwards. It is a delicate organ, but despite this, it forces its way through the soil, ever downwards in its quest for dampness.

At this early stage the root cells are squarish, are growing rapidly, each dividing into two, so that the rootlet as a whole does not grow, but only elongates as a result of the new cells added to it. It is, therefore, soon only a short region behind the point that is actually putting on length. This region of actively growing cells is called the primary meristem and since the root will soon have to grow in thickness, a secondary meristem arises forming a thin cylinder of cells inside the root right back up to the point where it left the seed. These cells will grow and divide sideways to thicken the root, but the growing layer always remains thin because, as the new cells are formed, the older ones nearer the centre take on other functions. The cells of this meristematic tissue, since they are growing and dividing and giving rise to new cells specialized to do particular jobs, are said to be undifferentiated.

The young root cannot long grow at the expense of the food-store in the seed but must fend for itself. Since surface soil normally contains but little water, the amount which can be absorbed will depend to a large extent on the amount of surface of the young root in contact with it. This surface being small has to be increased, so the outer cells grow long, fine projections, full of protoplasm and with very thin walls. These are the very important root-hairs which absorb water-dissolved nutrients from the soil.

The root-hairs are so delicate and so very important to the growth of the seedling, that to rub them off is to reduce the little plant's chances of living. When, therefore, small plants have to be moved to a new site they should never be pulled out of the soil but should be lifted out carefully with a small trowel or some such implement.

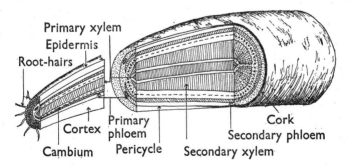

FIG. 5. *The change in a root as it ages.*

How, you may ask, does such a delicate organ as a young root manage to push its way through hard soil: even a pile, driven by a hammer, gets its point sadly worn during such a journey. Well, the point of the young root would indeed get badly damaged but, like a pile, it too has its point protected. It differs, however, from the pile in that its point is continually being replenished, the cells of the root-cap, as it is called, becoming mucilaginous, so protecting the root from friction caused by rubbing against the soil particles.

As the root grows, so it widens and the cells behind the meristem become specialized for carrying fluids up to the leaves (xylem tissue) and back from them (phloem tissue). The walls of the cells towards the centre of the root become thickened and strengthened by layers of a woody substance known as lignin. The protoplasm in them dies and they have now only a strengthening function.

The older roots no longer absorb water directly from the soil; their function is to anchor the plant and to transport substances to and from the rootlets. At this stage they get covered by a protective layer of cork.

The absorption of water by the root-hairs is an interesting and important process, and although the water goes in with some force, in no sense is the mechanism of sucking involved. Indeed, the plant is quite passive during the process – when the conditions are right, it just goes on. To explain this process (osmosis, it is called) simply is not very easy, but we can start by imagining two containers one inside the other (comparable with the root-hair and the soil). Now each of these containers holds a liquid, but that of the inner container is a stronger solution, that is, has a higher proportion of salt or sugar, than the outer. The wall of the inner container is composed of a substance called a semi-permeable membrane which allows the passage of some molecules but prevents others of a larger size passing through. This membrane has myriads of very small holes in it, and through these the water of the weak solution passes and dilutes the strong solution. If the solution consists of two different molecules which will both pass through the membrane, each will do so until the concentration on either side of the membrane is equal. This process is known as diffusion.

Such is the 'determination' of the weaker solution to dilute the stronger that it will continue to force its way in against the pressure needed to hold up a column of water 32 ft. high. It is no wonder that weak plants can lift paving stones and break down walls!

Osmosis occurs in all living animals as well as plants wherever the passage of one fluid into another takes place. Even our digested food in the intestines passes into the bloodstream by this method.

The root already described, along with its branches, is the true or tap-root system. But obviously, this does not explain the roots which arise from cuttings of stems when planted. Roots arising in this way are called adventitious roots and are first formed in a group of cells called the pericycle. Gardeners take great advantage of the ability of a stem to develop such adventitious roots, because new plants can be obtained more quickly from stem-cuttings than from seed, especially in the case of the woody plants. There is a further advantage in raising new plants from cuttings, for then they will be exactly like the parent plant, whereas if raised from seed some unwanted variations may arise.

A simple way to get a woody plant to produce adventitious roots is to peg down a branch into the soil, a process known as layering. A slight cut or constriction with a bit of wire at the lowest point will help the formation of roots. When adequate roots have been formed the branch can be cut off and planted as a new individual. Chemical substances have been discovered and are now on the market, which speed up the formation of adventitious roots. These will be discussed in a later chapter.

In a few cases leaves (e.g., begonia) will form adventitious roots or even leaf stalks, giving rise to new plants.

When you lift a turnip or a carrot to eat for the food that is in it, you should remember that the food was not put there by the plant for you. It normally has neither formed flowers nor seed by the time you lift it – it was expecting to do that the following summer, so it had spent the past one making the store of food for future use. Such plants are known as biennials.

Lots of plants make extra food and the root seems as good a place to store it as any, since it is reasonably safe there from winter cold and the depredations of animals.

The Shoot

Soon after the root has grown out from the seed the shoot appears and grows upwards to the light and air. Its form will depend on what sort of plant it is. The flowering plants (that is, all green plants other than ferns, mosses, liver-worts and algae) are divided into two groups called respectively the gymnosperms and the angiosperms. The angiosperms are again divided into two groups, the monocotyledons, with one seed-leaf, and the dicotyledons with two. The former include the grasses, tulips, onions, palms and other similar plants which normally have parallel leaf-veins and the flower-parts in threes. The latter include plants whose leaf-veins form a network and whose flower parts are often in fours or fives. There are internal structural differences as well, but they need not be gone into at the moment.

If, then, our seed is that of a dicotyledon the young shoot will bear two seed-leaves. These may not be at all like the next and succeeding leaves for the first two are usually very smooth, hence the gardener's instructions not to move the young plant until the first two 'rough' leaves appear. This is really a very good guide because by the time they have appeared the young root will have made considerable growth.

The young shoot, then, will first appear with two leaves and a bud between them. Rapidly the stem elongates, the bud gives rise to two more leaves but still there is a bud between them. This bud is the growing point where the undifferentiated meristematic tissue is growing and dividing, increasing the height of the stem and leaving behind it specialized cells which form the xylem vessels and phloem tubes through which water and its dissolved salts will come from the soil and down which will travel the substances produced in the leaves. There will also be left behind, a ring of meristematic tissue (the cambium) for increasing the stem's thickness and, as this takes place, new conducting, strengthening and protective tissue will be formed.

6

THE STEM

RATHER THAN TRY to explain solely in words all the diverse tissues in the stem of a plant, their arrangement and functions can be more simply and clearly understood with the aid of a diagram (Fig.6).

Epidermis is the outer protective layer which, in trees and shrubs, becomes replaced by the bark which is a corky layer. In many herbaceous plants and annuals the epidermis is covered by a waxy layer known as the cuticle.

Cortex is a protective layer which is thin in stems but very thick in roots.

Vascular bundles – separate groups of cells in young stems and roots consisting of phloem, cambium and xylem.

Phloem tubes conduct downwards the products made in the leaf. If this layer is cut through, by rabbits or mice, the sap will run out and the tree will die.

Cambial cells are meristematic. They grow (1) outwards, increasing the thickness of a stem and laying down new or secondary xylem behind them and a layer of phloem in front; and (2) sideways, until they meet cambial cells from adjacent bundles. Thus they form a ring not only of cambium but phloem and xylem tissue.

Xylem vessels behind the cambium carry water and its dissolved substances up from the roots to the leaves. In trees the xylem tissue towards the centre becomes woody and does not function as conducting vessels.

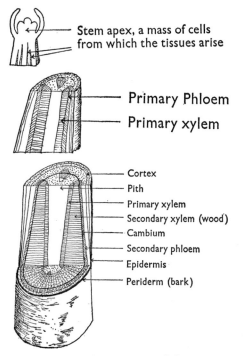

FIG. 6. *The development of the stem.*

Since growth is seasonal in temperate countries such intermittent growth is shown by the rings on the cross-section of a tree trunk and the age of the tree can be told by counting them. It is even sometimes possible to say whether the tree has had a good or bad growing season by the width apart of such rings.

Pith is the central mass of loosely packed cells. These are quite obvious in many plants which do not undergo secondary thickening, but in woody plants they tend to be crushed and disappear.

We talk of herbaceous and woody plants, implying that the former are without wood, but this is by no means always true. In many herbaceous plants wood develops in the lower parts of the stem.

Though stems may be of many shapes, the internal structure is basically the same for all dicotyledonous plants. The points on the stem where the leaves arise are called nodes and the areas of stem between nodes are known as internodes. These nodes are important because not only does a leaf arise from them, but in the axil of the leaf there may be a bud which, in time, will grow out into a branch. Therefore it can be said that whatever arises in the axil of a leaf (that is, the angle between the leaf and the stem) is a branch, even if it has the form of a spine, and whatever arises from below a branch is a leaf whatever form it may be in. An exception is to be seen in *Metasequoia glyptostroboides* where the bud often subtends the leaf. Thus the spines on gorse may be either leaves or branches.

The stem or its branches may be in one of many forms, for besides the usual upright form which is plain for all to recognize there can be the following forms:

(1) The underground stem or rhizome. This kind is found in Solomon's seal, couch grass and many other plants. It runs horizontally under the surface of the ground and at intervals sends above the surface leaves and flowers. As the rhizome travels so does it send out abundant adventitious roots and this is what makes couch grass, for instance, such a pest to the gardener: every little bit of rhizome left in the soil will produce new roots and send up new leaves and so continue to choke out other plants. Control can be obtained by means of certain selective herbicides based on dalapon.

(2) The runner is a rather slender stem running along the surface of the ground. Buds occur along it and from below each bud adventitious roots grow down into the soil and thus new plants are formed. The strawberry is the classical example of this mode of what is called vegetative reproduction.

(3) The sucker is similar to the runner but is underground. Mint is a plant which travels far by this method.

(4) The offset is a runner which produces only one new plant at its end instead of a whole series. It is the vegetative method of reproduction of the house-leek.

Besides the foregoing, there are other stem modifications which may be classified as storage organs for they contain a reserve of food, laid up in the summer and used to give the plant a good and early start in the following spring (Fig. 7):

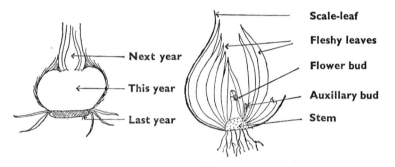

Next year

This year

Last year

Scale-leaf

Fleshy leaves

Flower bud

Auxillary bud

Stem

FIG. 7. *Crocus corm* (left) *and onion bulb.*

(1) Bulbs are the thickened lower part of the stem surrounded by thick, fleshy leaves full of reserve food. In the axil of these leaves there is, of course, a bud. Some of the buds may open and give rise to a new plant alongside the parent one. Examples are lily, onion, tulip, hyacinth.

(2) Corms are also a thickened part of the stem beneath the surface of the soil, but they are not surrounded by fleshy leaves. After the spring's growth exhausts the current one, another is formed above it and logically it would seem that sooner or later a corm would appear above the soil's surface. But adjustment is made; the plant has contractile roots which pull the new corm down into place again. Thus corms (and bulbs) of the same species of plants are found to occur at about the same depth, and since this is

the most suitable for the plant, it is worth the gardener's while to know approximately how deep each kind grows in nature so that he can plant to the correct depth.

(3) Tubers. The potato tuber is an underground stem-branch which has become swollen with a store of food. Its stem-nature can be seen by the presence of buds ('eyes') from which new shoots will grow.

All the cabbage family store food in the stem to some extent and because of the amount of food stored in marrow-stem kale we grow that plant as cattle-fodder.

Other Stem Modifications
   (1) Branches modified as spines have already been noted.

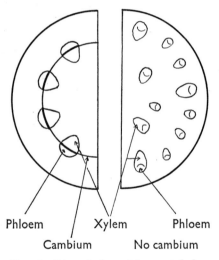

Phloem   Xylem   Phloem
       Cambium   No cambium
FIG. 8. *Dicotyledon : Monocotyledon.*

(2) Tendrils. Sometimes a branch may be in the form of a climbing tendril and when this is so it will be seen to bear very tiny scale-leaves. In the case of the Virginia creeper the tendril is thought to be derived from the terminal bud.

(3) Phyloclades. In the butcher's broom the branches become flattened and green and look like rather stiff leaves. That this is not so is clear on examination, because the flowers and fruits are borne on the middle of those 'leaves'. The flowers and fruits also arise in the axils of very tiny leaves so these must be branches. These are often called cladodes, a term strictly used for similar structures of unlimited growth.

The stems of monocotyledonous plants do not normally become thickened like those of the other flowering plants, and if a section be cut through the stem of one of them the reason becomes clear. Unlike the dicotyledons the vascular bundles are not in a ring but are scattered about, so, were a cambial layer to be present in the bundle, it could never grow in such a way as to join them all together and allow thickening to take place (Fig. 8).

There are monocotyledons, of course, which do have thick woody stems (the palm trees), but they achieve their thickness by growth of the cortex.

7

THE LEAF:
CHLOROPHYLL – LEAF SHEDDING – LIVING
SPACE – OTHER LEAF FUNCTIONS – BUDS

THE NORMAL LEAF is a thin, flat structure composed of an upper and lower continuous pavement of cells enclosing a number of regular cubic cells (palisade layer) and a more openwork mass of other irregularly shaped cells, through which runs an ever-branching network of vessels (the veins), which are continuous with those of the stem and root. On the lower side of the leaf there are numerous openings or stomata; although this is a somewhat general definition.

It is often said that the leaf is the factory of the plant and this statement, unlike so many popular ones is largely true. In the leaf of the green plant the world's food supply is made, and though the great petroleum refineries we hear so much about are important enough, they are quite unimportant as compared with the leaf-factory. It can make the three essential foodstuffs, carbohydrates (sugars and starches) fats and proteins and though the chemically simplest is sugar, even the Russians can't make that, though we know they can make a Sputnik! We know the principle of the sugar-making process but still we cannot make it, far less make fats and proteins.

But firstly we must have some clear idea as to what those three substances are.

Carbohydrates which include sugars and starch, and even this paper, are composed of the substance carbon and the gases oxygen and hydrogen, the last two being present in the same proportions as in water (simple sugar being $C_6H_{12}O_6$).

Fats, which includes plant oils and animal fats (but not mineral oil), are also composed of carbon, oxygen and hydrogen, but in quite different proportions.

Protein we know best as lean meat, but all plants contain some of it in other forms while the beans, and especially the soya bean, are rich in it. It is basically composed of the same three substances with the addition of nitrogen. All three form our, and every living things' food and from whatever immediate source it is got, it ultimately came from a green plant.

Now let us look at what happens in the leaf. Water is taken into the roots and carried up to the leaf. There it meets carbon dioxide gas which diffuses into the leaf from the air through the stomata. The two substances mix and energy is now needed to make them combine into sugar – a lot of energy – and this comes from the sun or special artificial sources.

Chlorophyll

However, some other factor must be introduced to encourage the union for if mere sunlight would do, every soda-water syphon left on the window ledge would become sugar if not toffee any summer day. This other factor is the green colouring matter of the leaf, chlorophyll. It makes the union take place quickly and efficiently: such a substance being called a catalyst. We can prove that the energy of light is necessary to the process simply by covering for a time part of a leaf with some light-excluding substance and then testing the leaf for sugar – it will be found in all parts of the leaf except the shaded part. To show that chlorophyll is equally necessary we need only test a variegated leaf whose green parts will give the reaction while its white parts will not.

The production of proteins and fats is extremely complex, based on a combination of carbon, hydrogen and oxygen with the addition of nitrogen. This combination is known as an amino acid, the details and reactions of which are beyond the scope of this book.

This process in which light is used as the source of energy is known as photosynthesis.

The chlorophyll which is so characteristic of green plants is a substance of considerable complexity and though it is green it may, depending on the quantities of its various constituents present, appear somewhat differently. Thus there is associated with the green colour two others, red (due to carotene) and yellow (xanthophyll) and sometimes, as in the copper beech, these will mask the green.

Sometimes, as in variegated privet, patches of the leaves are without chlorophyll and give to the plant what some people consider to be an added attractiveness. Likewise when, instead of such absence of colour, patches of carotene or xanthophyll appear in otherwise green leaves, greater beauty is achieved. Indeed, some multi-coloured leaves are exceedingly lovely.

In normally green plants chlorophyll is sometimes absent and this is likely to be due to a lack of magnesium and/or iron in the soil. Magnesium forms the centre of the structure of chlorophyll whilst iron is essential for the formation of green pigments. But even with those present in abundance chlorophyll will not be formed in the absence of light, hence the exclusion of light to blanch such vegetables as celery and sea-kale.

Chemically, chlorophyll acts as a catalyst, which is defined as a substance which speeds up a reaction but does not itself take part in it. We use a number of such catalysts in our digestive process, and platinum is one of the common catalysts used in industrial processes.

Leaf Shedding

We have seen how the leaves arrive on a plant and the next logical question is why they fall off trees and shrubs which do not themselves die down. The answer is that they are doomed to do so as soon as they are formed. As the summer passes into autumn a corky layer begins to develop at the base of the leaf-stalk and grows slowly inwards until all the edges meet. This leaves the leaf hanging on only by the thin vascular bundles which hold it to the branch. These sever as the leaf is blown about by autumnal winds, and the plant achieves its bare winter conditions.

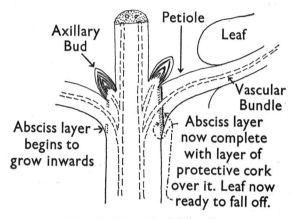

FIG. 9. *How a leaf falls off.*

This process takes place in all leaves; the evergreen conifers do it with less seasonal regularity; the holly waits for the spring; some forest trees may shed even their branches by this method when the season has been very dry.

The reason for this process is not fully understood but it is likely to be related to light intensity and temperature as it occurs at the end of the year. It is part of the normal cycle of plant growth, for merely dead leaves do not always fall off, as you can see by taking a leafy branch from a tree and leaving it to die then its leaves stay on.

Living Space

Since the green plant makes much of its food from carbon dioxide gas in the air, and must also breathe oxygen from the air, and since sunlight must strike its leaves, it is obvious that it must have space around it. Too often plants in a garden are crammed

D

together with the result that due to lack of sunshine (light) and perhaps nutrients, through competition, they grow tall and feeble, etiolated: a heavy shower or a medium breeze knocks them down into a tangled and unsightly mass: their blooms are scattered up the long stems and their flowering period is shortened. It is cheaper, easier and altogether more satisfactory to space plants in the flower garden or the kitchen garden at intervals which bear some relation to the normal business of the plant, though excessive spacing can be wasteful and encourage weed growth.

Although roots are hidden from the critical eye, they too need space and since the lateral extent of their travel roughly corresponds to the normal width of the plant, generous spacing is necessary for them too.

A plant growing in a pot, since it is almost in a specially created world of its own, should be living under ideal conditions, but how often is this so? How often does one see a straggly, foot-high plant in a four inch pot? Think of its roots, tangled like a bird's nest round the inside of the pot, while the owner calmly says, 'That plant is not doing at all well'.

As they grow in size, plants should be re-potted regularly to give them root room and to replenish the long-exhausted soil.

Other Leaf Functions

The plant, like all living things, has to breathe, for no sooner has it made food as shown above but it has to break some of it down again to get the energy which is locked up in it and which is necessary for all vital processes. Let us look at it this way—

Carbon dioxide + water + sun's energy = sugar + oxygen given off.

Sugar combined with the oxygen taken in $\rightarrow$ carbon dioxide + water with energy set free.

Now, we can put these processes into chemical terms, thus:—

Food production— $6CO_2 + 6H_2O + ENERGY(sun) =$
(catalyst—chlorophyll)

$$C_6H_{12}O_6 + 6O_2$$

Respiration— $C_6H_{12}O_6 + 6O_2 \rightarrow$ ENERGY(674 cals.) + $6CO_2 + 6H_2O$

The oxygen used in this latter process comes from the air and enters through the same stomata on the under-surface of the leaf. Under normal conditions the stomata are widely open during the day when both processes are going on, but are more or less closed at night when there is, of course, no photosynthesis taking place.

You will note from the above equations that the plant takes in and gives out the same substances as we do, therefore plants sharing a room with us also share the oxygen supply and help to increase the amount of the waste gas, carbon dioxide. From this has arisen the idea that it is dangerous to have plants in a bedroom at night. This is absurd, for the plants to make any appreciable difference there would have to be an awful lot of them in a very small and air-tight room. I have heard of people who would have a dog in a bedroom but would turn out a daffodil!

A further stomatal function is the getting rid of the surplus water which has been streaming up from the roots to bring to the leaf the raw materials of the food and enough water to keep the soft protoplasm in the living cells suitably supplied. Since this surplus water transpires through the leaves, it is called the transpiration stream. If for any reason (shortage of water in the soil or excessive evaporation from the leaves due to strong wind or high temperature), this stream is much reduced, the cells guarding the stomatal openings become flaccid and the openings close. This helps to conserve the water.

Buds

At the apex of the stem and in the axils of the leaves are the buds. They are of two kinds, buds which will give rise to new branches and the elongation of the main stem and those which will give rise to flowers.

In the case of the first kind, which are called vegetative buds, a future long stem is telescoped into a very short length, for every such bud is composed of a number of rings of crumpled leaves, each with a tiny lateral bud in its axil. All branch off from the shortened stem so that, though the nodes will be there, the internodes are so short as to be almost non-existent.

At the top of this shortened stem is the growing point of undifferentiated tissue which will, as the bud expands into a normal leafy stem or branch, keep on forming a terminal bud.

Since buds have to pass through the storms and frosts of winter and since they contain delicate and important structures, the closely overlapping leaves afford considerable protection to these parts. But since that protection may not be enough, the bud is often further protected by leaf-like bud-scales and even with a layer of some gummy substance. This is well seen on the buds of horse-chestnut and the pines.

Because buds are potentially actively growing parts of a plant they are often used for propagation, singly in 'budding' or a group in grafting when it is decided to grow one plant on the established root and/or shoot system of another. Single buds are also used as 'leaf bud cuttings'.

All buds, however, do not grow into new branches; many spend years, or even the life-time of the plant, in the same state and because of this, they are called dormant buds. But if some damage occurs to the plant above those buds, they may become active and develop into shoots. Thus, in making a hedge, a row of plants is put in the required position and allowed to grow. Each one will, of course grow upwards and, if left, the hedge will be a thin, straggly line of badly shaped trees. Long before this happens, however, we cut off the uprising shoots and this causes the dormant buds lower down to begin to grow and so the thickness of the hedge is increased.

Flower buds do not differ fundamentally from leaf buds except that their scale leaves enclose the parts of the future flower in cramped and unfinished form. On trees and shrubs it is usually easy to distinguish the flower bud from a leaf bud; the former is often larger and more rounded, leaf buds being long and slim or very small.

Practical Work

1. *The Root.* (a) Plant some beans in damp sawdust. After they have germinated take one out carefully and rinse it in water. Note the root-hairs which give it a fuzzy appearance.

(b) A week later examine another and do the same again for several weeks, noting the change in relative position of the root-hairs. Drawings should be made.

2. *Osmosis.* (a) Tightly tie a piece of thin cellophane over the end of a thistle-funnel. Pour a strong salt solution into the end of the tube until the thistle is full. Place the thistle in a beaker or tumbler of tap-water. Record the rise in water in the tube against time.

(b) Take a piece of the flower stalk of a dandelion. Split it longways and put one piece into a dish of tap-water; put another piece into weak salt solution and another piece into a strong salt solution. Note and draw their behaviour. Can you come to any conclusion as to why they behave as they do?

(c) Sow some seeds on damp blotting paper in two separate saucers. When they have germinated add a strong salt solution to one lot and compare the condition of the two lots of seedlings in a few hours. Make notes and drawings and explain.

3. *Storage.* (a) Test for starch. Boil up in water a piece of the tissue to be tested (although a potato tuber is not a root it is convenient for this purpose). Allow to cool, then add a few drops of iodine. If starch be present the solution will turn blue-black.

(b) Test for sugar. To a solution of the substance in a test-tube add a little Fehling's Solution A, then add a larger quantity of Fehling's Solution B. Now boil the mixture and if sugar be present a red precipitate of copper will be formed. It is best to start this experiment with an original solution of glucose in water.

4. *The internal structure of the root and shoot.* (This can only

be done if a microscope or a microprojector is available.)

(a) Examine prepared microscope slides of a young root and a young shoot of a dicotyledon before secondary thickening has taken place. Make labelled diagrams of the parts.

(b) Compare the foregoing with slides showing secondary thickening.

(c) Examine sections through the root and shoot of a mono-cotyledon, make drawings and compare them with those of the young dicotyledon.

5. *Twigs.* Examine, draw and label the parts of twigs of different kinds of shrubs, noting nodes, internodes, buds and their position on the stem and whether any structures have become altered (thus, spine = leaf). Among others the following should be examined – apple, horse chestnut, currant, goose-berry, hawthorn, gorse, butcher's broom.

6. *Underground stems (rhizomes).* Examine and draw examples of underground stems. Which common flower would you select?

7. *Bulb and corm.* Cut vertically through a bulb and a corm, draw and label. Take the bulb apart and note the thick, fleshy leaves. Look for buds in the axils of those leaves.

8. *Starch formation.* Cover the free end of a leaf of a growing plant with silver paper and leave it in bright light for at least a day. Remove the leaf from the plant and kill it in boiling water. Remove the green colour in warm alcohol. Pour iodine solution on to the leaf and note that the part of the leaf which was exposed to the light gives a reaction for starch, the part which was covered does not.

Try the same experiment with variegated leaves.

9. *Buds.* (a) Cut a bud (a brussels sprout is a handy size) through vertically and note nodes, internodes, leaves, buds.

(b) Cut open a flower bud, draw and compare with the foregoing.

8

FLOWER FORMATION

AFTER THE PLANT has attained a certain size, flowers will be formed, but when this happens depends on what sort of plant it is. If it is:

(1) an annual, the seed will germinate in the spring, the plant will grow up, bloom, set seed and die in the same year;

(2) a biennial, it will not normally bloom during the first year but will use its leaves to make a great amount of food. This is stored safely through the winter and, with the spring, leaves again appear and are followed rapidly by the flowers and seed, after which effort the plant dies. This ability to store food over the winter is taken advantage of, by gardeners, in such plants as carrot, turnip and cabbage;

(3) a perennial, it may live for quite a few years (or only one) before producing its first flower. After that some may carry on doing so annually for many years.

The flower, therefore, is the last stage but one in the life story of the plant. It is a critical stage too, because on its success depends the formation of the all-important seed. Since seed-formation is a sexual process involving the fusion of male and female cells (pollen grain and ovule), these have to be brought together and, because many pollen grains are carried by insects, the form, colour and perfume of the flower is such as to attract them as efficiently as possible.

(In some plants, such as *Thalictrum* and a few others, the female cells develop into seed without the stimulus of the male cell. This behaviour is known botanically as apogamy, and is similar to the production of young by the unfertilised female green-flies.

Now let us consider how the flower is formed to this end. A leaf bud is essentially several rings of whorls of similar leaves attached to a very short stem with a growing point. The flower can be considered as a leaf bud without a growing point and with some of the leaves altered so that though some may retain their leaf-like characteristics (the lower whorl, the sepals), the succeeding whorls become less and less so. Thus the petals, though more or less leaf-like in shape, are not often so in colour; the next whorl, the stamens, can be thought of as leaves, only the mid-rib of which remains and that is thickened at the top to produce the pollen grains; the last or centre whorl may look more like a knob than a ring because it is formed of a number of leaves, usually thickened, with their edges joined together so that

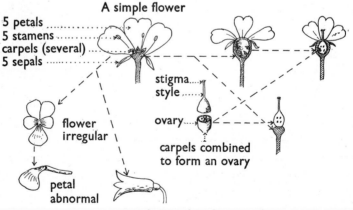

A simple flower

5 petals
5 stamens
carpels (several)
5 sepals

stigma
style

flower
irregular

ovary

carpels combined
to form an ovary

petal
abnormal

petals joined to form a tube

FIG. 10.

they form a box in which the ovules are developed. The centre of the top of this box is produced into a stalk (the style) whose end is slightly swollen (the stigma) and produces a sticky, sugary solution to trap the pollen grains.

The foregoing is the general plan: the details vary to an almost infinite extent, though there is a close similarity in each plant family. It is in fact, on such similarity that plants are classified.

The sepals are normally green and leaf-like, but they may be coloured like the petals or completely absent.

The normal shape of a petal is that of a leaf with its end notched instead of pointed, but it may vary to almost any extent and even in the same flower the petals may be of vastly different shapes. Their colour, as everyone knows, may range through the spectrum but we can make some mild generalisations, namely, that those pollinated by night flying insects will tend to be white: if they are coloured, they will attract the insects by producing their perfume at that time. In early spring when conditions may be favourable, flowers will be coloured with the 'simpler' pigments – white and yellow mostly, with some blue. Indeed, I have been told by a past Director of Kew Gardens that the majority of the garden flowers about the time of Queen Elizabeth I wore these simple colours. Our present-day galaxy of colour is due to selective breeding and sometimes treatment of the soil.

There is less variation in the stamens but the ovaries may be single 'boxes' such as we see in the buttercup when the petals have been shed. Each contains a single seed; but if several such boxes or carpels are fused together at their edges we get one large, multi-seed box as exemplified by the poppy.

Both stamens and ovaries may be and often are present in the same flower so it might seem that self-fertilisation would be bound to happen. This, however, is not so and most plants take steps to avoid it. The simplest and commonest method is for the pollen to ripen before the ovule (or egg). But the sexes may be in separate flowers on the same plant so that either the stamens or the ovaries are non-functional in each kind of flower. The most extreme case, of course, is when the sexes are on different plants. This last method can bring trouble to the unwary gardener who decides to have, say, a holly tree.

Care must also be taken when planting fruit trees for some apples, pears and plums produce pollen which is useless to themselves – not compatible, but will fertilise other varieties.

All sweet cherries are self-sterile so two compatible varieties must be planted for pollination and fruit set to take place.

It is therefore possible to have a tree which flowers annually but produces no fruit. Luckily, nurserymen are all out to help the novice and they draw attention in their catalogues to such peculiarities. In these cases it is essential that two suitable varieties be planted.

The Flower of the Monocotyledon is essentially the same as the dicotyledon except that the parts are in threes. Sometimes there may appear to be six petals as in the tulip and narcissus but these can be seen to be in two whorls of three. In the dicotyledon the parts are in fours or fives mostly, or some multiple of five.

9

POLLINATION – GERMINATION – VERNALISATION

Pollination

THE PROCESS of pollination involves only the transfer of the pollen grain from a stamen and its arrival on the stigma. Now, a pollen grain is a very small object and a stigma may not be a lot bigger, so when we realise that many plants rely on the wind to carry out the transference we must also realise that vast quantities of pollen have to be produced. Possibly one of the best ways of seeing this is to walk for a short distance, wearing black shoes, through a field of grass in June and July, or a heather moor in mid-August, when the pollen will fall on your shoes in collectable quantities: or in a smaller way, shake some ripe hazel catkins over a polished table.

All plants, however, do not depend on the chances of suitable winds but rely on the help of insects, some using any one, but the majority having a special insect, usually a bee. The bee, being a honey gatherer, is attracted to a flower if it knows it will get something when it arrives there. These flowers produce nectar (a sugary substance) and make it available to the bee, but may force it to enter in a special way. Whatever this may be, it involves the bee touching either the stamens or the stigma (or both). Since it has probably been to other flowers of the same species and will possibly be going to more, pollen will be transferred from one to the other.

In a large orchard where there are thousands of flowers in bloom at the same time, it is not safe to depend on the chance arrival of bees, so the owner often finds it worth while to keep a few hives, were it for nothing else than the certainty of having all the flowers pollinated. Sometimes orchard owners who are not bee keepers will hire a few hives and have them placed in his orchard.

Plants grown in greenhouses and frames may not be available to insects and if fruit is wanted (tomatoes, cucumbers, and so on) the gardener has to perform the pollinating operation. Cucumbers and melons have flowers of different sexes, so self-fertilisation cannot take place. The gardener, therefore, arms

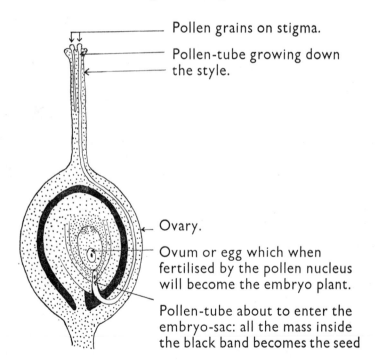

Pollen grains on stigma.

Pollen-tube growing down the style.

Ovary.

Ovum or egg which when fertilised by the pollen nucleus will become the embryo plant.

Pollen-tube about to enter the embryo-sac: all the mass inside the black band becomes the seed

FIG. 11. *Fertilisation and seed formation.*

himself with a small fine brush or a rabbit's tail which he first dabs on the stamens of the male flower and then on to the stigma of the female.

Hothouse cucumbers wanted for eating must not be fertilised and male flowers should be removed from the plant, whereas melons, marrows and outdoor (ridge) cucumbers must be fertilised to develop fruit to eat.

Once the pollen has arrived in the sugary solution on the stigma it begins to grow out a long tube. This bores its way down the style into the ovary and ovule, and there its nucleus fuses with that of the latter and a seed begins to develop. This is the fertilisation process which has to happen to every ovule if a seed is to be produced. After this the other parts of the flower, their work completed, wither away. Great activity now takes place, for not only has the young plant to be made of hundreds of cells resulting from the division of the original ovule, but a store of food has to be laid down and the whole wrapped snugly up in a strong waterproof case. Fertilisation and the resultant development of a seed is a very complicated process and the foregoing description is of necessity a simplified one.

The activity triggered off by fertilisation is not, however, confined to seed formation, for the rest of the fruit has to be developed (a fruit being the seed and all that is around it). If the outer case is going to be succulent like a plum, the ovary wall begins to thicken and become juicy. This is so planned that some animal will carry it away and eat it as far as possible from the parent tree: the discarded stone (seed) may then find itself in a place not overburdened with plum-competitors.

Many fruits are of the succulent type, but not all are made from the thickened ovary wall. Apples and rosehips, for instance, are parts of the stem which have been stimulated by the fertilisation process to grow up and surround both ovary and fruit, while the fleshy part of the strawberry is but a stem with the fruits embedded in it.

Other ovary walls become hard nuts or leathery (peas when ripe); some develop wings (sycamore) which slow their rate of fall from the tree so that they have a chance to be wafted from under the parental shade.

The Seed and its Germination

Legions of seed pass through the gardener's fingers in the course of a lifetime, though I suspect that many gardeners have but little idea of what is inside their hard coat.

Taking the seed of a dicotyledon first – a broad bean will do excellently – one need do no more than look at it, noting the hard coat and the scar marking its late attachment to the pod. Before further investigation can be made it must be soaked in water to soften it. It swells in the process and if it is now examined closely on the edge near the scar, it will be possible to see the little hole through which the water entered. This hole is the micropyle.

On removing the seed coat, the contents will appear as two fleshy, leaf-like structures (the two cotyledons, in fact, which are loaded with a store of food to give the young embryo plant a good start off in life). It is this store of food, of course, which makes the bean-seed so valuable to us.

The embryo is the white, comma-like object holding the two fat cotyledons together. If examined carefully it is possible to see at one end of it a faint, leaf-like fold (the shoot plumule) and at the other the baby root (radicle).

Most of the garden monocotyledonous seeds are far too small to be examined in this way, but if you happen to grow maize for the delightful corn-on-the-cob, one such seed laid on its edge and cut down with a sharp knife will expose an embryo, but this one will be embedded in a single mass of food reserve.

Let us return to the broad bean. It is put into the soil and there it lies until conditions for germination become suitable. This merely means slight warmth, sufficient air (oxygen) and some moisture, and spring conditions will supply these. Obviously, however, if the soil is cold and you plant deeply, germination will be delayed until the heat of the weak spring sun is able to penetrate the greater depth to stir the embryo to activity. But all seeds do not necessarily like the same temperature conditions. Spinach, for instance, likes a steady temperature around 60 degrees F., but carrot and parsnip and some other vegetable seeds require a varying temperature and probably warm days and cool nights fulfil these conditions in nature.

When the optimum conditions occur germination will begin, the seed absorbs water and at the same time the embryo sends out a sort of digestive juice – an enzyme into the food store. We have already seen that the green leaves of the plant are a factory producing sugar, but if sugar was stored it would make a very bulky plant. If the sugar could be condensed, less space would be needed, also a store of sugar in cells would cause a considerable upset in the osmotic relations between those cells. Starch on the other hand is less bulky and being almost insoluble does not effect osmosis.

The chemical formula of sugar is $C_6H_{12}O_6$ and from this it is possible to draw a molecule of water, H_2O, thus leaving $C_6H_{10}O_5$ which is starch, whose bulk is that much smaller. This process of subtraction of water from sugar and the addition of water to starch is not just done by drying and wetting but must be done with the aid of the enzyme diastase. (We have such an enzyme (ptyalin) in our saliva for turning starch to sugar.)

The embryo, then, sends its enzyme into the food store, changes starch back to sugar and begins to absorb the sugar, then growth takes place. The rapidity of this process is greatly affected by temperature and for rapid growth there should be distinct warmth.

Seeds, for these reasons, should not be planted deeply and as a guide it is often advised that small seeds should be only their own thickness underground. They should also be planted in a finely broken down soil which should then be pressed firmly down. This age-old advice is formed on sound reasons, namely, that the young root gets a firm anchorage, that it is brought into close and constant contact with the water in the soil, to make sure that the water passes up to it. It must also be remembered that a seed and young roots need adequate oxygen and this is lacking in the lower areas of soil.

Many seeds germinate almost as soon as they are shed from the parent plant; other seeds, however, may have to pass through a development period because of the fact that the embryo is not completed at the time of shedding. This happens in the case of the lesser celandine. In others the seed-coat slowly hardens after shedding, so that it takes much longer for water to enter and soften it again. For this reason holly seeds lie in the ground for two years before germinating. Some seed coats become so hard that water cannot enter them at all and in order that it may do so such seeds have to be filed or rubbed with sand paper, which is known as scarification. 'Morning glory' and some nuts are examples of this.

For reasons unknown to me the seeds of other plants may lie dormant in the ground for years and suddenly when the land is dug or ploughed, these seeds germinate and crops are choked by some unexpected weed. Charlock is possibly the worst offender in this way, but shepherd's purse has the same habit.

Some seeds, too, can remain alive for years if kept dry and so free from attack by moulds. Wheat seeds will live in this condition for more than ten years, and a few kinds may exist thus for almost 100 years. No seed can be dormant and germinate after 1,000 years, so the persistent story about the germination of ancient wheat from the tombs of the Pharaohs will not bear investigation. I have seen such seed and it is black and structureless: I have even planted some, but needless to say it was a waste of labour.

Before being sold some seeds are now tested for their 'percentage viability' (in other words what proportion is alive and likely to germinate), so the gardener is safeguarded against buying trash.

Vernalisation

It has been found that the period between germination and flowering in certain plants can be shortened considerably by a process called vernalisation. To do this the seeds are allowed or encouraged to begin germinating by keeping them wet. When the germination begins the temperature is dropped to around 35 degrees F. and kept there for about ten weeks. If the seeds are now sown in the usual way they will come to the flowering stage approximately a month before those sown in an untreated state.

This process has been used with wheat and has allowed the Russians to grow that crop farther north than before, extending into regions where the summer is too short for normal ripening of wheat.

Practical Work

1. *The flower.* (a) Draw a buttercup flower; dissect it carefully, draw and label the parts noting stalk, receptacle, sepals, petals, stamens, carpels.

(b) Examine the base of the petals for the nectaries.

(c) In the stamens note the filaments and anthers.

(d) Note the short style and the stigma of the carpel.

(e) Open an ovary and note the ovule.

(f) Repeat (a) – (e) with a wallflower and with an iris or a daffodil.

2. *The inflorescence.* (Fig. 12). Collect a number of different kinds of flower and note their arrangement on the stalk. They may be solitary, that is, a single flower at the end of the stalk, e.g., crocus. They may, however, be arranged in a group called the inflorescence, which may be one of eight well-defined kinds.

(a) The simplest inflorescence is the simple raceme, in which there is a main stalk, continuing to grow, and giving off flowers from below upwards. The oldest, therefore, are the lowest and the youngest (and last to open) is at the top. The lupin is a good example of this.

(b) the compound raceme is like the foregoing, but where a flower would be given off there is a branch which itself is a simple raceme. This is common among the grasses.

(c) The corymb is a simple raceme in which the lowest flower-stalks are the longest and the upper the shortest, so that all the

E

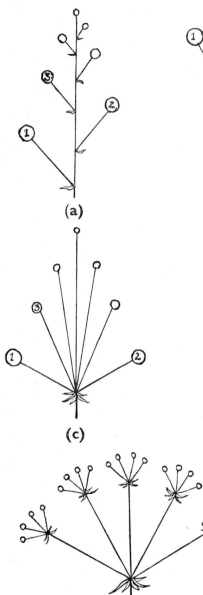
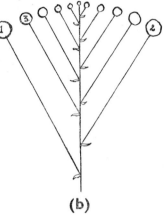
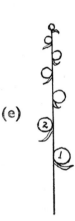

Fig. 12. *Some types of inflorescence:*
(a) *simple raceme;*
(b) *corymb;*
(c) *simple umbel;*
(d) *compound umbel;*
(e) *spike.*

flowers are brought to the same level to form a platform, e.g., candytuft.

(d) In the umbel all the flowerstalks arise from one point (the stem apex) to form a corymb-like platform, e.g., cowslip.

(e) The compound umbel has a number of stalks arising from the end of the flowerstalk, but each of these in turn gives rise to a number of smaller stalks on which the flowers are borne, e.g., wild carrot.

(f) If the flowers of a simple raceme are sessile on the main stalk, i.e., have no stalk of their own, the inflorescence is a spike, e.g., plantain.

(g) If the end of the flowerstalk is flattened so that the flowers appear to sit on a platform, like the 'flower' of a daisy, it is a capitulum.

In all the foregoing it is the lowest (or outermost in the case of the corymb and umbel) which opens first. But in the cymose inflorescence (cyme) the flower at the end of the stalk is formed and opens first; later, flowers are given off down the stalk, so they open later. The buttercup is a good example of a cyme.

At the base of each flower, or flowerstalk (peduncle) on the main stalk, there is a small leaf-like structure. This is a bract.

3. *Fruit.* Draw a gooseberry and note the remains of the flower parts. Cut the fruit into two horizontally, draw and note the position of the seeds. Do the same with an apple and note that it is a false fruit – why? Other available fruits should be examined and drawn, noting whether they are true, false, simple or aggregate.

4. *Seed.* (a) Soak a broad bean in water overnight. Draw side-view and edge-view showing the scar of attachment to the poit (the dark, narrow oval mark). Below it is a tiny hole (the micropyle). If the seed is squeezed gently water may be seen coming out of this hole.

(b) Remove the outer coat of the seed (the testa) and note the two fleshy leaves or cotyledons. Separate them gently and note that they are both attached to the small embryo plant.

(c) Separate the cotyledons completely. The embryo will remain attached to one. Examine it with a pocket lens and note the young root (radicle) and the young shoot (plumule).

(d) Examine a seed of maize. It is a monocotyledon, so there are not two seed-leaves. Note the position of the embryo.

(e) Fill a jam-jar with damp sawdust. Push into it some bean and maize seed so that they are in contact with the glass and are visible. They will soon begin to germinate. Note the two seed-leaves of the bean and the single one of the maize.

10

TROPISMS – ABNORMAL PLANTS –
INSECTIVOROUS PLANTS

Tropisms

IT MAY SEEM odd to talk about the 'behaviour' of plants. Why, you may say, plants don't behave in any particular way – they just stay put and grow!

However, I am afraid there is a little more to it than that. Remember that we have already mentioned two aspects of plant behaviour when we said that the root always grows down, while the shoot always grows up: plant a seed any way you like and still this will happen. Even if you put an iron plate below a growing root, though it certainly will not penetrate the plate, it will grow along it till it comes to the edge and then it will just as certainly turn downwards.

Such forms of behaviour may be simple, but all are not easily explained. In the foregoing the root is reacting directly to the pull of gravity while the shoot is reacting negatively to the same force. That this is so can be proved by placing a young, actively growing plant horizontally and rotating it slowly. By this means, though gravity force is not actually eliminated, it is made to act equally all round the plant, which will then continue to grow horizontally. Such reactions to simple forces are called by the botanists forced movements or tropisms, since there is no evidence that the plant shows any particular likes or dislikes in the matter.

One can see that there are really three aspects of this gravity reaction because, besides the two mentioned, there is the indifferent reaction shown by many branches which grow out horizontally. This is very clearly seen in most pines. But though a pine will grow to a great height with its normal apex always at the top and no branch ever trying to usurp its place, note what happens if the apex is removed – at once, one or more branches begin to bend upwards and take on the leadership. Mostly only one succeeds, but sometimes two and rarely three achieve the coveted position.

This behaviour on the part of the pine branches – years of horizontality then, in the absence of the leader, sudden verticality – was long a puzzle. It is now known that the apical region produces a controlling substance (a hormone or auxin) which makes its branches indifferent to the force of gravity. But once the hormone ceases to perform, when the tip is removed, the first branch-tip to feel the effect will turn upwards. Now it, in its turn, will produce the hormone and, so to speak, keep the other branch-tips in subjection.

A root appears to be able to feel the concentration of water in the soil and will grow towards it, especially when conditions are dry. Thus the roots of trees and bushes will tend to find drainage pipes in fields, grow into and ultimately choke them. The pull of water may be so strong as to overcome the pull of gravity and sometimes accounts for the death of seedlings carelessly watered in dry weather. Under dry conditions, the seedling's roots are badly in need of water and they will go after it: the gardener then decides to water them and, being a knowledgable man, he will give them a good soaking so that the water will go well down. If, however, he thoughtlessly only lightly waters them, so that only the surface layer is wetted, the roots may turn upwards into the wet zone. If a few days are allowed to pass before they are watered again they will begin to grow downwards again, but

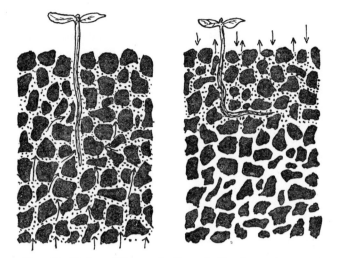

FIG. 13. *If the soil is evenly damp* (left), *the root grows straight down; but if the soil is watered too little* (right), *the root bends to keep in the damp zone.*

they may be too late and so die of drought. In fact, rather than water seedlings lightly and intermittently, it is better not to water them at all.

Phototropism, the reaction of plants to light, is not fully understood and indeed several factors may be involved but it is basically a chemical response. The movement is initiated by an auxin or growth-regulating substance. It might appear that light inhibits growth though a more likely explanation is that in the absence of light, cells grow larger. If a small area of a lawn is covered with a box for a few days, the grass beneath will be taller than that uncovered, but it cannot be said that the excess growth, 'drawn up', is entirely due to absence of light.

Shade, of course, has a similar effect so that plants growing under larger ones will tend to be 'drawn up'. Let me hastily add that I know that some plants do quite well in shade and even prefer it, but they are in the minority.

It is the absence of light on all sides which makes the pot-plant on the window-ledge bend over so irritatingly as if it wanted to get out. Let us analyse the bending behaviour. The light from outside falls on the side of the stem tips nearest the window: growth of the cells on that side will in consequence be slower than that on the shaded side and, therefore, the latter will grow larger and the tip will be forced over to the window. If, as in the gravity experiment, the plant could be slowly and constantly kept turning it would grow up perfectly straight.

Leaves, on the other hand, normally grow at right-angles to the direction in which the light is coming, so the light strikes their surface. This is important because the light is necessary for photosynthesis.

There are other types of movement in plants not due to outside forces. During growth the tips of some plants do not grow straight up but sweep round in a circle (really a spiral, of course). This is most noticeable in climbing plants and since the tip by this method is exploring a considerable amount of space, its chances of meeting some suitable object to cling to is greatly increased. Tendrils do this, too, and when the tip comes into contact with a solid body it very quickly bends round it. This is due to hormones which cause the cells farthest away from the object to multiply rapidly.

It was earlier mentioned that most living plant cells are kept rigid by being swollen out with water, so any reduction in the water pressure will cause movements in the plant. Thus in the barberry, when an entering insect touches the base of the stamens, the pressure suddenly alters and the stamens jerk up and throw a shower of pollen over the insect.

The night closing of the leaves of many plants such as oxalis is also due to a reduction in pressure in the cells, and these are called 'sleep-movements' because they normally occur at night.

Flowers also often close at night, for example, the tulip, crocus, flax, water-lily, oxalis and many more. Those pollinated by night-flying insects open at night, for example, the evening primrose and night-scented stock. Salsify has the odd habit of closing at noon.

Mimosa pudica or sensitive plant can be induced to produce such sleep movements by shock, which lends interest to the plant as a greenhouse specimen.

The causes of all cases of this kind are not always clear, and I have been unable to find one simple factor controlling the opening and closing of the flowers of mesembryanthemum.

Abnormal plants

Strange blooms and strangely coloured leaves may be attractive to the gardener, but I think that strange behaviour with its associated structures may be equally so, and most of these arise through living in unusual places.

There are few parts of the earth's surface which do not support plants of some kind and if the conditions are odd the plant may be odd too. Although extremely arid regions such as the great sand seas of North Africa and the gibber deserts of Australia are virtually devoid of plant life, other deserts (more accurately called 'semi-deserts') support a wide variety of plants adapted to arid conditions. Some of these plants are tank-like, storing water to last them through the long periods of drought. Water-storage may occur in the leaves, stems or roots. *Penio-cereus*, a Mexican cactus genus, has a huge swollen root-stock surmounted by thin, twining stems. Many other cacti have globular or cylindrical succulent stems but not leaves, whereas the Echeverias and other succulent *Crassulaceae* have thickened leaves which are protected from desiccation by a waxy cuticle. The surface areas of the leaves or stems of succulent plants are reduced so as to minimise the loss of water by transpiration.In extreme cases the leaf or stem is reduced to an almost spherical shape as in the *Lithops* of South Africa (leaf succulents) or the *Mammillarias* and many other cacti of the Americas (stem succulents).

The flowers of succulent plants are often extremely gay. The flowers of the *Cactaceae* are mostly brightly coloured and quite conventional in appearance (those of the Opuntias resemble roses), but some of the other succulent plants produce quite unusual flowers. The Stapelias from Africa have striking blossoms, usually large and starfish-shaped, which are luridly coloured in brownish-purple and yellow and have powerful and repulsive smells. The odour of carrion from these flowers attracts blow-flies which effect pollination.

Cacti, apart from a few species of the epiphytic genus *Rhipsalis*, are natives of the New World where they are indigenous from the southern borders of Canada to the Chubut territory of Argentina. The majority of cactus species can be grown quite easily in Britain as long as they are protected from frost and from excessive damp in winter. Indeed, many are frost-resistant if kept dry in cold weather. Some Opuntias and the 'peanut cactus' (*Chamaecereus silvestrii*) are practically hardy and can be grown outdoors all the year round in the south of England.

There is no special difficulty in the cultivation of cacti. A good soil mixture consists of three parts of John Innes No. 2 compost with one part of sharp sand. Water should be given generously during the growing season (April to September). Little water is needed during the winter months, although care should be taken to see that small seedling plants do not become completely dry. In hot weather frequent watering and spraying will keep the plants lively and fresh.

Cacti and many of the other succulents can be propagated easily. Seed germinates readily in moist soil at about 70 degrees F. Cuttings can be taken which should be allowed to dry until the wound is calloused over before insertion in soil or in a peat-sand mixture. Leaf succulents such as Echeverias can be propagated by simply detaching leaves and placing these on the soil-surface. Plantlets are readily produced in this way, the old leaf slowly withering away. Some species of *Kalanchoe* produce plantlets at the tips of leaves still attached to the parent plant.

There are several native succulent plants in Britain, including the Stonecrops (*Sedum* spp.). These are creeping, mat-like plants with succulent leaves which colonise cliff-tops, rocky ledges, walls and other places which have 'micro-desert' climates since they may receive no water for weeks at a time during the summer months.

Another 'difficult' habitat for plants is pure peat. Here, it will be remembered, there is an over-abundance of organic matter which will not break down because the acids created by bacteria stop further bacterial action. To grow successfully in peat, most plants have recourse to the help of mycorrhiza, that association between the root-cells of a plant and a fungus mycelium, which will be discussed later. Rhododendrons are dependent on such a mycorrhiza and they grow best in lime-free soil, especially if their roots are well surrounded by either peat, leaf-soil or other organic matter in which the mould can get its nutriment.

Insectivorous plants

Other plants under those conditions have developed animal-like feeding habits. If we define a plant as an organism which makes its own food from simple substances in the soil and air, and an animal as an organism which uses already made food, then the fly-catching plants have wandered a little way out of our field!

There are three genera and perhaps ten species of such animal-eating plants in Britain. Of these the sundews (*Drosera*) are the most spectacular. Though small, their leaves bristle with little projections like tiny pins whose heads produce a sticky fluid which traps small flies. Once there, the leaf folds inwards like our fingers towards the palm and so brings other pinheads into contact with the victim. Digestive juices are poured on it and, when digested, it is absorbed and only the hard outer skeleton is left.

The butterwort fly-catchers have a flat rosette of long, pale-green leaves, but they have no pins. The whole upper surface of the leaf is sticky and when the insect is caught the leaf-edges roll inwards until the digestive process is completed.

Such plants introduced into the garden should have a specially made bed of the kind they are used to, namely, boggy peat for the sundew and drier but rather poor soil for the butterwort. In these, the shortage of available nitrates will encourage them to keep up their fly-catching habits.

There are other more elaborately devised fly-catching plants in which the leaf, or part of it, forms a beautifully designed trap. The best known of this kind is the pitcher-plant from the eastern tropics. In it the tendril at the end of a leaf is modified to form a container which may be of pint capacity, fitted with a fixed, open lid whose function is probably to keep rain out.

The lip of the pot is very smooth and is fitted with downward running ribs a little raised. Inside and just below this area are nectaries to lure insects, especially ants, to try to walk down the smooth surface. If they do not slip off this surface and fall into the pitcher, they next meet a peculiar waxy surface which crumbles as they tread on it, so now they are bound to fall in!

The bottom of the pitcher contains some fluid in which the insects drown, then the great numbers of digestive cells in the lower part of the pitcher's walls pour digestive juices into the fluid and so digests the poor unfortunate.

The pitcher plant (*Nepenthes*), being from a moist tropical country, will grow only in a heated greenhouse. Its substratum should be sphagnum moss and peat placed in a hanging basket. It requires plenty of water and a moist atmosphere.

A collection of fly-catching plants would make an unusually interesting kind of garden, because this peculiar habit is not confined to land-plants but is found among water-dwellers too. *Utricularia*, the bladder-wort of our streams, is a case in point. In it, of course, the catching method has to be different from that of the land forms, if only because a sticky substance or slippery surface is not very effective under water.

Just as we invented the eel-trap with its narrow mouth and inwardly projecting ring of spikes so, ages before us, the bladder-wort had invented the same device! Its trap is also a modified leaf. However, since the plant lives wholly in water and since the traps are very small the plant may be of more interest to the aquarist than to the gardener.

11

PARASITES

PARASITIC PLANTS are not of much interest to the gardener, but a little must be said about them, if only to note how this particular habit causes modifications in a plant.

If we consider the common dodder which infests clover, nettles, gorse and other plants we find that the seed does not germinate until the host-plants have already grown to a reasonable size. The young root grows quickly down and the young shoot-tip travels in ever-widening circles as it elongates. If it meets a suitable host-plant the dodder twines round it. Once in position it sends suckers into the tissues of its host and draws from it all the necessities of life. Then since it is no longer wanted, the root dies and for the same reason the leaves remain as small, brown scales. It does have to produce seed, however, so it produces abundant little flowers.

Production of vast quantities of seed is necessary for an organism living this type of life because, in order to carry on the race, some plants must find a host, for unless they do so, the race is extinguished.

Superficially, ivy behaves in a similar way towards adjacent plants, but it is not a parasite. It may kill a tree but not because its suckers penetrate and draw out the tree's food, but because its mere constricting pressure against the expanding, living

77

tissues of the tree interrupts the flow of sap to the roots.

Mistletoe (Fig. 14) is a partial parasite only. Though it grows on and takes much of its nutriment from its host by the suckers which it sends into the branch on which it is perched, its leaves are green and do to some extent make food for itself.

The sticky pulp round its seed is an interesting method of dispersal. Birds carry off a fruit and, having eaten it probably on another tree, wipe their beak on a branch and in the process stick the seed on a new site.

Neottia, or the bird's nest orchid, is found growing in woods where there is a good depth of decaying leaves. In this plant the leaves do not develop and there is no chlorophyll, but since it is

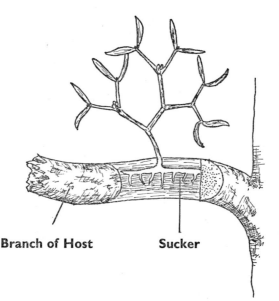

Branch of Host   **Sucker**

FIG. 14. *Mistletoe is one of the partially parasitic plants. Although it bears green leaves, and is able to manufacture some food for itself, it also sends suckers into the branch of the host plant, often an apple or oak, from which it receives much of its nutriment.*

not living on a living host it is not a parasite, but is known as a saprophyte. It must, however, get its food somewhere and if it cannot make it, something else must, and this is again mycorrhiza which breaks down the dead leaves and passes some of the food it makes to the orchid.

In this case, however, the fungal threads seem actually to penetrate into the cortex of the plant's roots and it has been noticed that, though many of those threads are quite normal, some are partly digested as if they have been attacked by the plant.

The wild orchids of our countryside are perfectly normal plants, but they, too, are closely associated with the fungal mycorrhiza and the story of the germination of their seed is almost a fantasy.

The seed of an orchid is extremely small and it does not germinate easily. Once it has germinated it is attacked by the mycorrhiza which does not merely adhere to it, as happens in most plants, but actually bores into it and begins to destroy it. That part of the fungus outside the orchid is busy making food from the humus in the soil and passing it to that part of itself in the plant. Thus the young orchid may be destroyed, but on the other hand it may suddenly begin to attack and destroy the fungus, receiving in the process the benefit of the fungal food and tissues.

Now fortified, it puts on some growth. But as this slows down, the fungal attack is renewed, and so the battle goes on for several years during which no part of the orchid has yet come through the surface of the soil. This period may indeed last for ten years or more, so it is little wonder that raising orchids from seed is not a popular activity.

This underground growing stage without the ability to make sugar and other foods, forces the plant to dependence on the other organism which can work without chlorophyll. This has suggested the experiment of germinating orchid seed in sterilised soil, where no fungi are present, and feeding the growing underground stem with sugar.

Agar and sugar solutions are now widely used commercially for raising orchids from seed.

Few gardeners are prepared to wait from four to sixteen years for an orchid to bloom, so propagation of this group of plants is by division of the bulb which should, because of the fungus, be given soil containing plenty of organic matter.

Practical work

1. *Geotropism.* Germinate some beans in sawdust as described in Chapter 7. When the root is about an inch long, remove the plant carefully and replace it so that its root and shoot lie horizontally. Note the time required for each to grow through a right-angle. When the new positions have been established, the plant can, if desired, be put back into its original position, when the root and shoot will change course again.

2. *Phototropism* and *Hydrotropism.* Attempts should be made to design a way of demonstrating these processes. Attempts should also be made to find the rate of reaction of the plants.

3. '*Sleep movements.*' *Mimosa pudica* (the sensitive plant) is easily grown from seed in a pot. It should be grown and its behaviour when touched noted.

4. *Fly-catching plants.* If any of the sundews can be obtained (they are common on wet moorlands), a plant or two will thrive in damp peat in a shallow vessel. The reaction of a leaf to a fly placed upon it is interesting (in nature it catches only very tiny flies, but it will digest a housefly).

12

CUTTINGS – GRAFTING – BUDDING – 'GRAFT-HYBRIDS'

PLANTS ARE NOT just static things which if left more or less to themselves, will produce flowers or fruit in due course. To get the best from them even to that extent requires care, thought and labour. But it is possible to interfere with the course of nature and get considerable amusement and interest in the process.

Perhaps the easiest way to find amusement in this direction is by inducing stems to produce adventitious roots or, in other words, to grow new plants from cuttings. A surprising number of plants can be grown in this way, some producing adventitious roots very freely.

It is also a very cheap way of getting new plants, and few indeed are the gardeners who will refuse to allow one to have a slip off an admired shrub.

In general, cuttings can be taken either when the plant is dormant, that is without leaves, or in the summer when it is actively growing. It is obvious that the same treatment will not do for both types.

Hardwood or dormant cuttings can be stuck into the soil and left until spring conditions stimulate them to life. But it is important that they should be firmly embedded in the soil; a loosely fixed cutting will never develop roots. The piece to be used for this purpose should be from one of the parent plant's side-shoots and should be six or eight inches long. If possible, the base must be cut cleanly with a sharp knife. The cutting so prepared is now inserted in a small trench in good soil on a slightly shaded site. It will assist rooting if one inch of coarse sand is placed at the base of the trench. The cuttings should be inserted to about half their length, the soil replaced and firmed around them.

In the case of summer or softwood cuttings, again taken from a sideshoot, the successful rooting depends on several factors:

(1) The growing stem must not be too soft or hard. If it is really soft and pliable it is no use and the same applies if it has gone quite woody. Indeed, it is very difficult to indicate the precise optimum state for such cuttings, and seasons vary so much. Practice, with its failures and successes, is the only guide.

(2) Since the softwood cuttings bear leaves there will be a considerable amount of transpiration; they are, therefore, more likely to live long enough to produce roots if they are planted under cover in a frame or under a cloche so that the atmosphere around the leaves can be kept very humid. Such softwood cuttings should be taken with a short part or heel of the previous year's growth attached to them.

In this type of cutting it is usual to remove all leaves which will be underneath the soil when it is inserted and to remove some of the lower ones from the part above soil level. Often when leaves are large the remainder are cut in half to reduce transpiration as much as possible.

Nowadays it is helpful to dip the ends of such cuttings from difficult plants in one of the root-forming hormone powders or solutions which help to stimulate root development. They should only be used if necessary (many garden plants root easily without) and in strict accordance with the maker's instructions because too much can be lethal to the plant (see Chapter 14).

In this connection it is amusing to think that those gardeners who were (and are) said to have 'green fingers', thereby indicating that most of the plants and cuttings they planted grew, were unwittingly using such a hormone. It appears that indole acetic acid, which is one of these hormones, actually occurs in small quantities in the excretion from human hands. There is very little, of course, but probably more in the case of some people than others and if one of the latter happened to be a keen gardener, well – he'd have 'green fingers'!

In actual fact, cuttings from some plants like currants and forsythia will grow with the greatest ease, even when planted in the open.

However, and despite the foregoing, I have had plants grow very successfully from cuttings of the most unorthodox kind when just stuck into the soil in the open garden, but such techniques should not be relied upon. Some have even been carrying blooms when they arrived after a three-day journey!

Conifer cuttings present a further difficulty because a mass of resin is apt to gather round the cut end and stop the formation of roots. This can sometimes be got rid of by quickly dipping the end into very hot water for a moment or by rubbing most of it off with sandpaper.

The advent of thin, water-proof plastic materials in sheets and tubes has made possible a technique by which shoots can be induced to form roots while they are still attached to the parent plant. Plants which are difficult to root by ordinary methods can often be propagated by this means. A handful of wet moss (peat if moss is not available) is laid on a piece of sheeting and the latter wrapped round the branch like a poultice so that the moss is firmly around it. The sheeting acts as a bandage to keep the moss in place and the bandage is tied round it and the branch. An even better way is to use a tube of plastic (polythene), slip the end over the shoot and fix the lower end round the stem with Cellotape, fill the tube six-to-eight inches long with wet moss or peat and seal the other end of the tube to the stem with tape. This method is known as air layering. The advantage of the plastic is that once the wet moss is firmly fixed it will remain wet and can be left in place almost indefinitely. Air can enter and CO_2 can escape but spores cannot pass.

Grafting

The process of grafting involves getting a twig or small shoot of one plant (the scion) to grow on another which already has a root (the stock).

Unfortunately, it is not possible to get other than closely related plants to grow together, so the idea of having plums, pears, apples and cherries all on the same tree is hardly a practical proposition.

Grafts can be made in various ways but they all depend on the principle that the cambium, which is the actively growing part of both scion and stock, has to be in close contact.

The simplest type of graft is made by choosing a scion and stock of the same diameter and then cutting each at a similar steep angle so that when the scion is placed on the stock, it will fit and be vertical. This simple splice is now bound tightly round with raffia to keep it in position till the union is completed, and covered in wax.

Open wounds, animal or plant, are very apt to let in bacteria and the spores of moulds. Once these get established they may cause considerable damage, and since in grafting the wounds are large, it is advisable to protect them with grafting wax or even clay plastered on.

Scions, needless to say, should always be small shoots, were it only because it is impossible to fix a big structure firmly enough to stand against a breeze. It is also harder for the stock to feed a big shoot, so the chances of a successful union are reduced.

If a small scion has to be grafted into a stock of considerably larger diameter it can be done by the wedge method. In this the end of the scion is cut into the shape of a wedge: the horizontally cut stock is now split downwards across its diameter with a sharp knife : the wedge end of the scion is inserted so that the cambium at one side of it comes into contact with the cambium at one side of the stock. The stock can now be bound up tightly and treated with wax as before. Of course, in this case two scions can be put on the same stock because there is a vacant space at the other end of the split.

These are two very simple grafts described briefly. For fuller details of the methods of these and more elaborate types, specialist books should be consulted.

Budding

Budding is merely another form of grafting in which a bud sliced off its parent plant with a 'shield' of underlying tissues is inserted under the bark and against the cambium of the stock.

This operation can only be performed in the summer when the bark of the stock will still come easily away from the stem, parting in the area of cambial tissue. A T-shaped cut is made and the two flaps of bark gently and carefully raised. The bud shield is now taken, and since it is most likely that a thin piece of wood has been cut off with it, this is gently prised off and the shield slipped into the opening between the flaps of bark on the stock. These are pressed down and tightly tied with string or raffia, and the whole can be waxed if desired but this is not necessary.

This method is much used in the propagation of roses, the bud from the named rose variety being inserted on the stock of a briar.

Propagation by grafting and budding is necessary when plants do not produce seed; when, if seeds are formed, it is unlikely that the offspring will be exactly like the parent; when a plant gets a better start and does better on an already established and vigorously growing root. In tree fruits, control of vigour and time of fruiting is secured also.

'Graft-hybrids'

It sometimes occurs when somewhat dissimilar plants are grafted together, that a bud arising near the union will develop into a branch which shows characteristics of both plants. At one time this was looked upon as being an actual hybrid between stock and scion, but now it is no longer considered as such but as a mere monstrosity or plant chimaera.

Such can be made by joining two plants with a wedge graft when the diameter of both is the same. This graft is treated in the normal way and when it has 'taken', the stem is cut across a little below the original cut surface of the stock.

Buds will begin to be formed at this cut surface and they may grow into branches of three kinds, namely, those containing only tissues from the stock, those containing only tissues from the scion and a few which may be composed of tissues from both stock and scion (Fig. 15).

If there is a stem-colour difference between stock and scion, this will show in the hybrid branch. I believe the union has been visible even in the fruit.

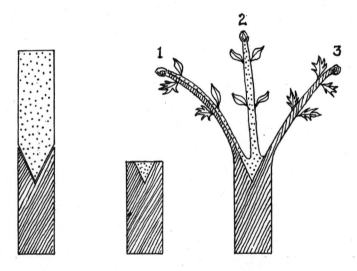

FIG. 15. *The making of a 'graft-hybrid'.* Left: *Two plants of the same diameter having been joined by a wedge graft; the dark lower part is the stock, and the upper part is the scion.* Centre: *This shows how the stem is cut across a little below the original cut surface of the stock after the graft has taken, leaving a small wedge of scion wood.* Right: *Growth forming at the cut surface, composed of three different types of tissue – 1, tissue of stock and scion; 2, scion tissue only; and 3, stock tissue only.*

Black nightshade (*Solanum nigrum*) grafted on a tomato plant (*Lycopersicum esculentum*) – both closely related – are favourite material for this kind of experiment. Common laburnum with broom grafted on it also tend to give chimaeras, an example being *Laburnocytisus adamii*.

Seed produced from such a chimaera give rise to one or other of the original plants depending on which particular tissue gave rise to the seed.

No doubt this peculiarity arises in nature and it has been suggested that plants with variegated leaves like those of pelargonium (the scarlet geranium) may be chimaeras. This, however, could be due to some chance mutation which could have arisen quite suddenly.

The whole question of 'graft-hybrids' caused a considerable stir in the biological world when it was a much-made-of tenet in the faith of the Russian botanist, Lysenko, but was not held in much esteem by botanists outside that country. Thus the results of plant grafting could give rise to international bitterness – to such a pass have things come!

13

GROWTH REGULATION:
CONTROLLING FLOWERING – PRUNING

REFERENCE HAS ALREADY been made to the encouragement of
root growth by treating stem-cuttings with indole acetic acid or
one of the other auxin substances which have the same effect,
and it is natural to ask how these substances affect the plant. Let
us look at it this way – certain plants like forsythia, currants and
willows root from cuttings very easily because their stems have
groups of cells called root-initials which, given suitable conditions, will form roots. Other plants have stems with few or no
root-initials, so, when their cuttings are planted, they may (and
mostly do) die before such initials can be formed. Root-forming
substances, however, when applied to such stems cause some
cells to form the initials fairly rapidly and so, of course, rooting
follows. Thus cuttings of apple, pear and holly can now be
grown with reasonable success, as a result of treatment with
those substances.

It is not possible here to go into the actual concentration of
root stimulators which should be used for each particular plant
because the amount of variation is very great. The point,
however, is that the concentration must be extremely small, one
ounce in two and a half thousand tons might be a little too

highly concentrated! Since these substances occur in urine one of the disadvantages of pouring the undiluted effluent from a farmyard manure heap on to young plants becomes obvious. All such fluids must be well diluted.

Once it had been found that one part of the plant could be stimulated chemically, it was natural that other parts – and chemical substances – should be experimented with. The fruiting spurs of fruit trees are branches or shoots which do not elongate, so if terminal buds could be treated in such a way as to keep them from growing, fruiting spurs would be formed and laborious pruning avoided. It would, of course, be undesirable to stop all terminal buds making extension growth, for the tree would never build up a framework of fruiting wood if this were done; therefore, this does not hold much practical value. Experiments, attended with some success, have been carried out with alphanaphthalene acetic acid.

These growth-promoting substances have been used in the production of seedless fruit. As has been shown earlier, the fruit is formed as a secondary result of fertilisation so that normally if seed is not formed there will be no fruit. It is now possible to get plants to form fruits by dusting or spraying them with one or other of these substances. This formation of seedless fruit is not, of course, unknown in nature – whoever saw a banana seed? – and such odd cases may be due to the formation of a growth regulator by the plant itself. Auxins are also used in sprays to prevent pre-harvest drop in apples, and to induce early apples to colour up before picking.

There is a large field here in which any interested gardener can experiment. And since it is known that tomatoes react to this treatment, there is an easily available plant to start with, but the production of seedless plums, raspberries, and indeed all the rest, offer a wide field in which to work. Any or all of the growth regulators could be tried, especially naphthoxyacetic acid (N.O.A.). Other regulators which inhibit growth are being made use of commercially. Coumarin, which is found in many plants and adrenalin made by animals, do this. They are used in the

U.S.A., and on the Continent for stopping the production of shoots in stored potatoes over which they are dusted in tiny quantities, and thus loss in the stored tubers is reduced.

There is another substance produced by plants which affects primarily their growth in length. This substance is called gibberellic acid. It has really been known for a long time in the East where it was found that rice plants attacked by a particular fungus, *Gibberella fujikuroi* (now known as *Fusarium moniliforme*), grew exceedingly tall. Investigation of the fungus showed that its effect was due to this particular substance which it passed into the rice plant.

Recently, however, it has been found that gibberellins are made by the plants themselves and, because of their power to increase the size of plants, great hopes were entertained about their effects. However, so far these have not been justified because, though they do cause many plants to elongate, the plants are thinner so there is no particular gain in plant material, and crops treated with this would have no advantage over the normal crop. Gibberellic acid does not control growth in roots.

It seems that gibberellic acid has some effect on seed germination. The seed of some varieties of lettuce will only germinate in the light, but if treated with gibberellin, they will germinate in the dark.

It may have some effect on the flowering of plants but it is not safe as yet to say much more about its powers for, as the lawyers say, the case is *sub judice* at the moment and much or little may still be discovered about it. A large amount of research work is going on at the present time on this substance, especially with camellias.

Controlling Flowering

It is known to all that some plants flower in early spring, some in late autumn but the majority in high summer. Why this should be so was rather a puzzle because, though it seems obvious that the process is directly linked with the light and temperature, this would appear not to be so, directly at least.

Many experiments were carried out to discover why there should be this diversity in flowering time but it was by accident that the real cause was found. This turned out to be the amount of light a day or, in other words, the length of the day, and it was also found that it did not much matter what the strength of the light was during that time.

Plants can be divided into three groups.

Short day group requiring daylight of 12 *hours or less* (flowering spring and autumn):

> Common primrose
> Chrysanthemum
> Snowdrop

Long day group, requiring daylight of 12 *hours or more* (mid-summer):

> Lettuce
> Beet
> Radish

Indifferent day group (any time):

> Tomato
> Wallflower

This reaction of the plants to the length of day is called photo-periodism.

Though the strength of light which counts as daylight does not matter, the particular kind of light does. White light, as everyone knows, is composed of waves and different lengths and when this white light is passed through a prism it is broken up so that its components are sorted out as colour-bands according to their length. Thus, violet occurs at one end of the spectrum and red at the other (ultra-violet and infra-red are invisible waves beyond those two colours), the violet being the longest waves and the red the shortest.

It has been shown that it is the yellow-red waves which most affect the time of flowering. It now looked as if the workers were getting to the root of the matter, when it was suggested that it might not be the length of day at all, but the length of the night which was the controlling factor! This seems to be borne out by the fact that the short-day-flowering chrysanthemums will not flower at all if a light is switched on during the night, even for a very short time. No sooner is such a fact discovered than we try to make use of it and this was no exception, because gardeners at once saw that if late-flowering chrysanthemums were wanted, all that has to be done is to switch on a light for a little while during the autumn night, then when plants are wanted to begin flowering they are left in undisturbed darkness! Could snowdrops be made to flower out of season, one wonders, by giving them a longer night under a darkened cover in summer?

Much work has been done to try to find out how the light actually affects the plants, and though a complete answer has not yet been found, it seems that it causes the leaves to produce a substance (another hormone provisionally called florigen) which then circulates up to the tip of the plant and starts the process. Anyhow, if light is excluded from the leaves flowering does not occur.

Pruning

The process of pruning generally applies to the woody plants and is carried out for one or more of several reasons. In the case of flowering shrubs it is imperative that, in many plants, pruning must be done to allow light and air to get right into the middle of the bush. In the wild state such pruning would not often be necessary because wild plants do not receive annual doses of manures and so their growth is not so vigorous. But the cultivated shrub has the greater food supply and will send out shoots in greater abundance and those more shaded than the others will tend to grow long and straggly until the shrub becomes unsightly.

If, as is likely, the shrub is grown for the beauty of its flowers, they will be small or short-lived if the food and energy which should have gone into their making have been diverted to the baser job of making wood. And here the first problem arises, namely, do the flowers occur on the new shoots or on the wood of the previous year? If they occur on the new wood pruning may be done as vigorously as required to keep the bush in shape, but if they occur on the old wood, thoughtless pruning will only make sure that there are no blossoms at all! Forsythia is a case of this sort, so it is safest not to prune at all, except in so far as to cut off branches which are grossly out of place.

It need hardly be said that pruning is sometimes necessary as a sort of surgical operation to remove dead and decaying branches. When a branch dies from the end it should be cut off along with a few inches of the living wood. If it is a large branch and not a mere twig, there will be exposed at the cut surface a large area for attack by rain and diseases, and to protect it, it should be given a coating of a bituminous paint (Arbrex).

The pruning of fruit bushes again involves no general rules because of the different behaviour of the various kinds of fruits, for to treat black currants and red currants, for instance, as if they were the same is going to land the unwary amateur gardener in a mess.

Red currants, and white ones too, bear their fruit mostly on the old wood, so they should not be allowed to produce great quantities of new shoots. At the end of the season all such should be cut back and in winter when the leaves have fallen off they may be again cut back to half a dozen buds. They thus increase in bearing capacity quite slowly.

Black currants, on the other hand, bear their fruit on the new wood, so, if treated like red currants, they will not fruit at all. In fact, the pruning must now be confined to cutting out branches two or more years old.

From the foregoing another difference will appear. Suckers should not be allowed to arise in the case of the red currants which should, so to speak, stand on one leg, whereas growth from the bottom does not matter in the case of the black currants; it should be encouraged.

Gooseberries bear the fruit mostly on last year's wood, so pruning is not necessary except where branches get too long and are apt to lie on the ground. But the gooseberry is also a spur-bearer and such forms as are markedly so (for example, 'Careless') can be pruned severely. Gooseberries should also stand on a 'leg' as with red currants.

Since raspberry canes do not fruit twice on the same canes, those which have borne fruit should be cut out and the best of the new canes staked in their place. These should then be topped so as to encourage the growth of branches and, consequently, more fruit.

Loganberries, blackberries and others of a similar kind should receive the same treatment as raspberries.

The larger fruit trees are merely pruned with the aim of increasing the fruit yield (of course, a certain amount is done to preserve the shapeliness of the tree). In pruning for fruit yield it is necessary to know where the fruit normally occurs: if on spurs, then they must be left, but if all along branches it is necessary to see that a great many lateral branchlets are not left to choke up the tree and use up food merely in making wood and leaves.

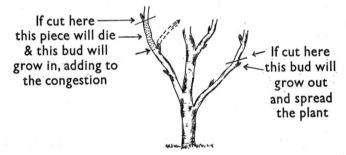

If cut here → this piece will die → & this bud will grow in, adding to the congestion

← If cut here ← this bud will grow out and spread the plant

Fig. 16. *Some points to remember when pruning.*

It is at the start of its life that the fruit tree is most difficult to deal with, because then it is growing rapidly and sending out branches freely. In such young trees, first decide which have to be left to form the main framework of the tree (the leaders) and cut them back to half length in their first year and less in the next three years. All branches which are not leaders should be cut back to half a dozen eyes (buds).

Sometimes, do what one likes, a fruit tree will produce abundant branches and leaves but no fruit. It is possible that this behaviour is due to too much manure being given to the tree, so the first thing to try is 'starvation'. If this does not work then it may be necessary to indulge in root-pruning. Go out from the base of the tree a distance of $1\frac{1}{2}$ to 3 ft. (depending on the size of the tree) and dig a trench halfway round it. This must be done with care: all fine fibrous roots are pushed out of the way, while all thick woody roots are cut through and, for preference, removed.

It is as well to attempt to tunnel under the tree and cut through the tap-root. All this having been done, the fibrous roots should be carefully put back with the soil and the latter stamped well down. If need be this can be repeated on the other side of the tree in two or three years' time.

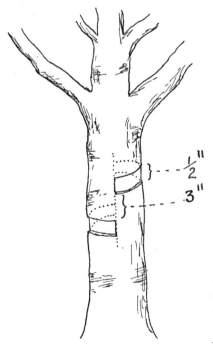

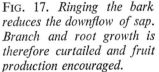

Fig. 17. *Ringing the bark reduces the downflow of sap. Branch and root growth is therefore curtailed and fruit production encouraged.*

Another method achieving the same result is to ring the tree (Fig. 17). This is done by making two parallel cuts with a sharp knife short of halfway round the trunk and removing the piece of bark between, down to the white wood. This cut should be about half inch wide. Below that at a distance of three to four inches make another similar excision, but round the other half of the trunk, so that the two half cuts do not overlap at their ends. This interrupts the flow of sap and growth-regulating substances downwards to the roots and retards their growth and the consequent upward flow of water with salts in solution to the branches and leaves.

If you feel that really drastic treatment is necessary, then extend each ring so that the ends overlap very markedly. Of course, if this is made too drastic the tree may be killed.

Practical Work

Adventitious roots. (a) Put a few cuttings of forsythia or currant into a jar of water and watch the development of adventitious roots.

(b) Take two cuttings from each of several kinds of shrubs. Dip the end of one into a solution of root-forming hormone (according to the instructions on the container); leave the other untreated. Put each into a separate labelled jar and note the comparative results.

14

MENDEL'S LAWS – POLYPLOIDY – MUTATIONS

SINCE LONG BEFORE the scientific era, as our age has been called, man, who differs from almost all other animals in that he must interfere with nature, has been experimenting with and improving his stock and crops. His methods were for long of a hit-or-miss variety, for he did not know the mechanism by which his results were achieved, but none the less he got results and that was the main thing. One has only to look at garden flowers noting their increased size and colour range, and compare them with the unchanged descendants of their wild forebears to realise to what extent improvement has taken place. Pictures of cattle, pigs and horses of a hundred or more years ago show the poorness of the material of that time and from what selective breeders have built up our present stock.

The hit-or-miss method certainly produced results, but such methods are wasteful of time and material and it was not until there appeared on the scene a man of high intelligence with a love of gardening and time to think, that an explanation of the mechanism of the selective breeding process was found.

In 1822 Gregor Johann Mendel was born. He entered the Church and ultimately became Abbot of Brunn in Moravia. In this job there was no hustle, and no exaltation of the trumpery: he could work or walk in his garden and notice things and meditate. The oddity of his garden peas seems to have caught his attention, for from the same lot of seed there were long stemmed and short stemmed plants. What was the explanation? He decided to investigate.

By taking seed (peas) from each group and sowing them separately, making sure that cross-fertilisation did not take place, he found that the long stemmed peas produced both longs and shorts but the shorts produced no longs.

He concluded therefore that the shorts were 'pure' but the longs were not. In other words he thought that at least some of the longs must contain two characters or factors, one of which was hiding the other. This he called the dominant and the other

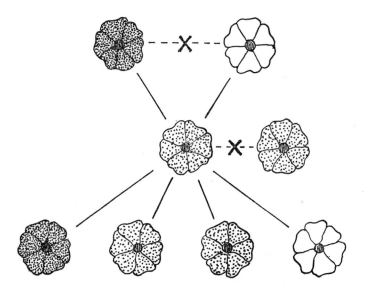

FIG. 18. *Simple Mendelism. If colour is 'dominant' to white, then the two top flowers crossed will give only coloured offspring. Any two of these crossed* (centre) *will give offspring in the ratio of three coloured to one white. But two-thirds of the coloured will be carrying hidden white and so will not breed true; only one-third will be pure and breed true. The white or 'recessive' will, of course, always breed true.*

the recessive. These could be written as L and l, representing long and short respectively.

If plants of only a pure strain are crossed we can only get pure offspring, thus:

        pure parents L L x L L or l l x l l
        offspring   L L   l l

But if we cross impure parents the results will be different –

    (1)   L l x L l   (2)   L l x L L   (3)   L l x l l
        LL, Ll, Ll, ll   LL, LL, Ll, Ll   Ll, Ll, ll, ll

In (1) there will be three apparent pure longs and one short (but two longs are impure).

In (2) they will all be apparently long (two longs impure).

In (3) there will be two longs and two shorts (no pure longs).

When normal pollination was allowed the result was as number 1 and gave the famous three to one ratio of longs and shorts. It can now be seen why this could happen and why the shorts never produced longs – they carried no factor for longness.

To understand how this works in the living plant we must go back a little. In an earlier chapter it was stated that plants are composed of cells and that each living cell has a nucleus. We go a step further and find that in the nucleus there is a group of rod-like bodies called chromosomes, whose number is fixed for each species of plant and animal – humans have 48.

Growth of a plant takes place by the division of its cells, and the first stage of this process is the disappearance of the wall of the nucleus: the chromosomes then arrange themselves in a circle in one plane; each now divided into two longitudinally: the two groups of halves migrate away from each other and become surrounded by a new nuclear wall and at the same time a plate is formed which divides the cell into two.

When, however, sex cells (pollen and ovule) are formed, the process is only the same up to a point, because now the chromosomes do not split: instead, they divide merely into two lots so that each new (sex) cell has but half the original number. The chromosomes carry the hereditary factors or genes from one

FIG. 19. *Cell division*. Above and below, from left to right: *cell enlarged showing nucleus; thread-like mass in nucleus; nuclear wall disappears; spindle forms with chromosomes; chromosomes split and the two sets divide, each going to one end of spindle; nuclear wall reappears, and a plate then divides the cell into two, each with a nucleus with an equal number of chromosomes.*

generation of the plant to the next; therefore, if a long-stemmed plant is considered it will be seen that one sex-cell may contain L and another l, or that all may contain only L.

The point of this reduction-division, as it is called, ensures that the new plant will have the same number of chromosomes as the parents when the two sex cells unite.

Working merely on the basis that each character of a plant is determined by one factor in a simple manner like this, would leave but little scope for experiment. But the fact is that lots of characters are due to a combination of several factors and that leaves plenty of room for trying things out.

Here I should like to return to the story of Mendel. He worked, of course, for years on his garden peas, dealing with the smoothness and wrinkliness of the seed in the same manner, and published the results of his work in the journal of the local natural history society, and there the matter temporarily ended.

Half a century or so later an Oxford Professor, William Bateson, was also puzzling over the problem and had come to the same conclusion but had not published his findings. At the same time another biologist, who knew of Bateson's work, was spending a holiday in Brunn and during one wet day, to pass the time, was glancing through the old natural history reports and was astonished to see that his friend's work had already been done by the local Abbot. When this was reported to Bateson he, to his credit, publicised his own and the Abbot's work under the name of Mendelism. Had that day been fine we would have been talking of Batesonism!

Having now got some idea as to how this cross-breeding works, things began to move more quickly, and in this as in other fields, there often arises someone (perhaps you?) with a special flair for manipulating it; such was Luther Burbank.

Burbank was born in the U.S.A. and died there in 1926. He was no scientist and never laid claim to be one, but he was deeply interested in nature and especially plants, and his interest in breeding them was stimulated and his whole life directed by reading Darwin's *Variation of Animals and Plants, under Domestication.* His experiment started when he was quite young and his first success was an improved potato. From there he went on, ever widening his scope, till he had experimented with many thousands of plants.

In the end he had produced new and improved varieties of apples, pears, plums, cherries and a great variety of garden flowers. Perhaps his greatest success was in the modification of some cacti. Those plants, though succulent, are heavily covered with strong spines and, though they are abundant in otherwise plant-free, arid lands, were utterly useless as food for grazing animals – no such animal could get past the forest of spines. Burbank, however, set to and succeeded in producing a cactus which had no spines. This, of course, changed the value of the desert lands so that stock could range where none had ranged before.

The satisfaction which he got from this work and indeed his whole attitude is summed up in his remark, 'I shall be content if because of me, there shall be better fruits and fairer flowers'.

Most of our new strains of plants are the result of careful, selective, cross-breeding. The loganberry is such a cross, having as its original parents the blackberry and the raspberry, but without going quite so far as this, much interest can be had by trying to produce garden flowers merely different from the usual.

The production of the famous Russell lupin was achieved by this method, and by a man who was no scientist, was poor but deeply interested. He was, in fact, a jobbing gardener who thought what wonderful flowers lupins would be if they had more variety of colour, so he set out to see what could be done about it.

He collected lupin seed from every possible source and grew as many colour varieties as he could find. Then he started crossing and re-crossing them, taking years in the process for, though an elderly man, he knew that hurry was pointless. Even when he had achieved something he would neither sell seed nor give up – perfection was what he wanted. He got it in time as every gardener knows.

Basically, the principle is to choose those plants with whose characters you are proposing to experiment. They must be closely related of course. When buds are formed and before they open they should be covered with a bag of very fine muslin to keep out insects whose help you certainly do not want. When the flowers open and the pollen is ripe, some of it can be removed on a fine paint brush (this, of course, refers to the artist's and not the decorator's kind): the brush so loaded is now wiped gently on the stigma of the new flower. It is often advisable to cut off with a pair of fine scissors the stamens of the latter flower. Seed should now be formed and must be kept carefully labelled for next season's sowing. Once something has been achieved it is perpetuated by inbreeding for obvious reasons.

There is nothing particularly difficult in the method of artificial fertilisation and most gardeners who grow peaches and tomatoes perform the process every season. But they are only interested in seeing that fruit is formed and if an insect helps them so much the better. In doing the work to achieve a special end, however, the precautions already mentioned have to be taken.

Hybridization has another function besides production of new plant-forms. It is well known that hybrids tend to be stronger and more free-growing than a long inbred race, so crossing takes place to produce this hybrid vigour.

Polyploidy

Despite what has been said about the reduction in the number of chromosomes in the formation of normal sex-cells, it sometimes happens that such cells are formed without reduction in chromosome number.

If such a sex-nucleus succeeds in mating with one with a reduced number or, as sometimes happens, one with an unreduced number, the resulting plants will have three or four times the number of chromosomes possessed by the original parents.

Such plants will show differences from the original kind and will not cross with it though they will with themselves. This means, in effect, that they no longer belong to the same species as their parents.

Mutations

So far we have assumed that changes in plants can take place only by a reorganising of the genes. This is not so, however. For the genes themselves can become altered by various forces or things impinging upon them, or even by what we might call inadequate reproduction of themselves.

We know that genes can be altered by subjecting them to

X-ray radiation and to the radiations from atomic explosions. Normally all plants and animals are subjected to such radiation from cosmic rays and from radioactive substances in the earth. These vary in intensity as to both place and time and, when the intensity is high, gene-alteration (or damage) may occur.

Some chemical substances such as caffeine, formaldehyde and mustard oil are also known to have the same effect, and all occur naturally in some plants.

Now, if the genes in a plant get altered it will not, of course, affect that plant in any obvious way. But it will affect the sex-cells, and if the change produces a dominant, it will appear in the next generation: if, on the other hand, it produces a recessive, it may exist for quite a few generations without showing itself and will only do so when it meets another similar recessive (cf. Mendelism).

Such sudden changes in genes are called mutations and are thought to be one of the main causes of evolution.

With nuclear explosions being set off in so many parts of the world today, and the amount of radiation to which all living organisms, and soil on and in which they live and the food they take in are subjected, they must be affected to some extent. It is possible that all are being affected and this, combined, for instance, with a heavy, local shower of cosmic rays, may increase the radiation to a dangerous extent and do some damage. When such damage will become apparent is quite another matter. If the radiation causes gene-damage which acts as a recessive it may be hidden for three or four generations in slow breeding animals like man, though it may appear sooner in annual plants. Obviously, the last word has not been said on this subject.

15

CONIFERS – FERNS – LIVERWORTS AND MOSSES

IN EARLIER CHAPTERS we have discussed flowering plants, dicotyledons and monocotyledons, but they are by no means the only
plants which go to make a garden. They are, however, the most
showy and have a higher degree of organisation than any of the
others.

However diversified the others may be, whether they have
mighty trunks and grow 100 feet high or are merely soft, leaf-like
blades lying flat on the ground, they have in common the one
characteristic, namely, they do not produce flowers. Within this
group of flowerless plants the method of sexual reproduction
varies considerably.

For convenience they are divided into the following groups
– conifers which include all the pine-like trees and which mostly
bear cones; ferns which have leaf-like fronds which produce
reproductive spores; mosses and liverworts which are simple
plants with little specialisation of structure.

Conifers

As garden plants the conifers are not often considered, I
suppose chiefly because one thinks of them as huge objects
which take up a lot of space. Well, of course, some of them do.

but others do not. It always seems to me that a conifer should be welcome in the garden if only because in the winter it remains green and, so to speak, keeps the continuity of plant life from season to season.

For those who cannot find the space for the larger forms as trees, the yew, the Douglas fir and cypress, *Cupressus macrocarpa*, will stand being clipped into hedges, the last growing at a remarkable rate. Many others such as the junipers are large and dignified enough to stand alone as 'specimen trees' ten to fifteen feet high on a lawn, or may be low, slow-growing shrubs suited to a rock garden. However, a list of species suitable for any particular type of garden, or place in a garden, can be got from the catalogue of any good nurseryman.

The conifers are an ancient race of plants whose fossil forms extend back some 250,000,000 years into the early Carboniferous Era. Those early forms were not always very like their present descendants as we know from a still living relic of that distant past which will grow freely in this country. This one,

FIG. 20. *'Trees' which helped to form coal some* 250,000,000 *years ago:* (a) *giant horse-tail which grew to* 100 *ft.;* (b) *two giant club mosses;* (c) *an extinct conifer; and* (d) *a tree fern.*

Ginkgo biloba or the maidenhair tree, was found in China growing in the temple gardens, it being considered sacred. It is not known to grow wild.

As its name indicates, it has a broad leaf, notched at the apex and resembling that of the maidenhair fern. It grows, in time, to a great height and has few openly spreading branches. It does not have a cone like an ordinary conifer but the fruit is rather like a white marble.

Though *Ginkgo* has been known and grown in this country since 1740, only a few years ago another living fossil conifer, *Metasequoia*, was found living in China. This tree is much more pine-like in character and grows well in this country. To me, at least, the very primitive antiquity of those plants lends a fascination such as I do not find in the nearest and loveliest productions of the present.

We must, however, return to a general consideration of the conifers and we can take the pine tree as our example.

The external structure of the stem and root are fairly similar to that of the dicotyledon. The most important difference is the presence of a ring of tubes running through the cortex outside the phloem. These tubes are needed to carry the resin made in the leaf which is a characteristic product of the majority of the pines.

The leaf is more primitive than that of the dicotyledons, having the stomata all over it instead of mainly on the underside. These are sunk in pits and so are shielded from stormy winds and, consequently, excessive evaporation. The outer layers of the leaf are tough and hard and the combination of these characters makes it possible for the tree to withstand difficult climatic conditions. For this reason the conifers can range higher up mountain slopes and further north than almost any other trees. In winter, too, they cover their buds with a heavy layer of resin which protects them very successfully from hard frost.

Typically, the seed is borne in a cone. This is a short stem carrying overlapping scales each with a naked seed under it and from which the conifers and their allies get their scientific group-name of gymnosperms or naked seeds, since they are not formed in an ovary. The cones we are so familiar with can be considered as the female flowers, while the pollen-producing male flowers are represented by smaller cones. These are ripe in May or June and at the same time the female cone becomes prominently exposed and the scales open so that the wind-carried pollen can reach the ovules. Once this has happened, the scales close down again and the cone bends back among the leaves. Fertilisation now begins but does not proceed very far before it stops for that year and only becomes completed in the following year.

All conifers do not, of course, have the same habits as the pines. The larches, for instance, lose their leaves every year, while the seed of the yew is most unlike a cone. Indeed, it is at first a single, uncovered ovule formed at the apex of a short stem and later partly surrounded by a fleshy case which grows up from its base.

There is much to be said, if space is available, for making a collection of conifers. They have such a wide range of form – from juniper to the monkey-puzzle tree – and colour (from dark green to blue), that they are full of interest even when the deciduous trees are bare sticks.

Ferns

In some ways ferns are nearer the flowering plants than are pines, and they are usually considered as the linking form in the evolutionary series. But ferns never bear flowers: instead, on their fronds – either on the back of the normal fronds, on special parts of the frond or on particular fronds set aside for that purpose – there are produced little cases which contain spores.

Now, we have talked a lot about seed, by which we mean a reproductive body resulting from the union of a male and female body. A spore, however, is to be likened merely to a small piece of the parent plant which is set free and will germinate.

It is a sort of structureless bud and is an asexual method of reproduction.

Once the spore (there are thousands of them, of course) of a fern is set free it is carried off by any breeze, for it is very small and light. If it lands in a suitably damp situation it begins to grow and forms a most unfern-like, flat, heart-shaped leaf applied closely to the ground. Its underside has processes (rhizoids) which grow down into and absorb substances from the soil, while the blade, tiny and green, makes them into food substances in the usual way.

This plant is the prothallus. It grows to about a quarter inch across and now begins to develop male and female reproductive organs on its underside. When the contents of these are ripe, a male cell is set free and swims to a female cell, driving itself through the thin film of water on the underside of the prothallus, by the lashing of a long thread-like tail of which it is possessed.

Once fertilisation is completed, a young fern plant begins to grow up from the prothallus which, its job having been performed, now withers away.

This astonishingly complicated behaviour is called alternation of generations and is much more common among living things than one might think. Fern spores can be produced in far greater numbers than seed: being lighter they can be carried over a greater area and their numbers make it likely that some will fall on a suitable spot, even if such spots be few.

Besides this normal method of reproduction, one often sees the fern, *Asplenium bulbiferum,* growing in pots, and this also reproduces vegetatively by producing great numbers of adventitious buds on its fronds. These in time break off or can be broken off and planted to give rise to new individuals.

Though ferns grow in damp, shady places it is hardly fair to them to stick them in any dark corner of the garden. They, too, need light, air, water that is not stagnant and mineral substances in the soil. If they are grown in pots they may need more water than ordinary flowering plants but they should get just as good drainage.

Although the ferns take a lowly place, both in size and numbers, in our flora this was not always so. They first appeared in geological history much further back than conifers and several hundred million years before the flowering plants.

The first fossil ferns appear in Devonian or Old Red Sandstone times about 300,000,000 years ago. The following warm, damp, climate of the Carboniferous period saw them flourishing in abundance, and with their high, woody trunks they must have dominated the landscape of the time.

In the following Permian times which were drier and more suited to the huge reptiles which then existed, the ferns became less abundant and luxuriant of growth. But as the climate again got wetter the ferns again became a dominant feature of our landscape.

But as the present day approached they faded to the comparative insignificant position they now hold. However, in the warmer parts of the world tree ferns may still be seen growing to a height of seventy to eighty feet with a tuft of fronds at the top, some of which may be twenty feet long! They are not all confined to warm regions because several reach high altitudes – even to the snowline in Tasmania.

Almost all our ferns would be tree-ferns did they not have their thick stem lying horizontally underground. Indeed, it sometimes gets a little above the surface, though seldom more than a few inches. The only case I personally know of in which a stem a couple of feet high has been achieved, is a royal fern beside a remote Highland loch. This particular stem is over a foot thick and bears a great number of crowns of fronds.

Liverworts and Mosses

These two last groups of green plants are of little interest to the gardener. The liverworts are flat, blade-like structures resembling the prothallus of the fern but on a larger scale. They differ from it, however, not only in size but in the fact that the blades can grow and branch indefinitely. Liverworts are always confined to damp places and may be found even in water.

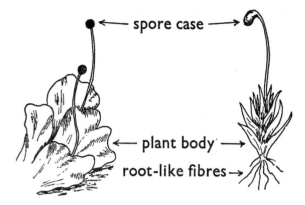

FIG. 21. *Two low forms of plant life which tend to be unpopular – a liverwort* (left) *and a moss, both showing spore cases.*

Mosses are somewhat more highly organised than the liverworts and are composed of apparent stem and leaves. But these are very simple structures compared with those of the flowering plant. Unlike liverworts, the mosses will grow in quite dry places.

From the point of view of the gardener mosses can be a great nuisance, especially when they colonise the earth in flowerpots and get established among small plants when it is difficult to get them out without tearing the other plants up too.

Mosses really become a pest when they begin to colonise lawns and though they can be eradicated by chemical means, they are nevertheless a bother. The rapidity of such colonisation by moss is due to the speed of reproduction by spores and also by the fact that they can reproduce vegetatively from any part of the plant which happens to come into contact with the soil.

The real cause of mossy lawns lies, of course, in the conditions of the soil. The moss plant, being a small and delicate structure, requires a good supply of moisture, so it will tend to grow in badly drained lawns. This is not, however, the only cause for mossy lawns; because of their delicacy, mosses cannot stand much competition, and if the soil is poor the grass plants will also be poor and will leave space which the moss plants can invade. The cure, therefore, is to have a well-drained, rich soil carrying good, strong plants.

Practical Work

1. *Pine cone*. Take a ripe cone and draw it. Break it across and then pull off some of the woody sections. Below each there should be a seed which should be drawn.

2. *Fern*. Examine a fern frond and note and draw the spore-cases on its underside. If different kinds of ferns can be got the position and shape of the spore-cases should be compared.

3. *Liverworts*. Lift a piece of earth on which liverworts are growing; examine and draw them.

4. *Moss*. Do the same with moss, and try to get some showing their spore-cases on stalks.

16

MOULDS – BACTERIA

MOULDS, WHICH INCLUDE mildews, belong to the great family of plants, the fungi, which contains the mushrooms, toadstools and such-like. They are however, somewhat more simply organised. Like all other living things they are composed of cells, but these, instead of being massed together to form organs, are attached end to end to form long chains, with each link in the chain similar to every other one.

Moulds are quite unlike green plants in their behaviour in that, for want of chlorophyll, they cannot build up their sugar from the simple substances of the earth and air: they, like us, have to depend on the activity of other living organisms – and basically the green plant – for their food supply. This means that they have to behave like us in that they are feeders on living or dead organic matter, and since that is in a too complicated form to be absorbed it has first to be broken down (digested). In our case, we take in the organic matter in its gross state and subject it to the action of digestive juices, absorbing into our blood-stream what is soluble and getting rid of the remainder. The moulds, however, being without a mouth and digestive system, pour out their digestive juices on to the organic matter and digest it outside themselves. This completed, they absorb only what is soluble and suitable to them. Moulds living thus on dead organic matter are called saprophytes.

Thus it is clear why moulds so rapidly cover any piece of dead organic matter and why they do so when such matter is damp. Stored seeds are obviously ideal food for moulds but only if moisture is allowed to get to them.

Some moulds have developed a most unusual way of life. They have linked themselves with the roots of some green plant so that a partnership is set up between the two in a state called symbiosis. It works in this way: the mould gets the energy it requires by breaking down the organic matter in the soil and in the process ammonia is split into simple nitrates. The green plant, via its roots, absorbs these necessary nitrates for its own use. The green plant, on the other hand, is able to make quantities of sugar which the mould cannot make, so in return for the nitrates it gets some spare sugar.

This type of mould is the mycorrhiza already mentioned. It is being found that more and more plants seem to depend to a greater or less extent on such moulds. It is possible, therefore, when a plant fails to thrive, do what you like, it may be that there is no suitable mycorrhiza in the soil so the plant is finding difficulty in getting an adequate supply of nitrates. It seems to me that this may well be the case with *Tropaeolum speciosum* which grows like a weed (it can be a real pest!) in some places; in others it will not grow at all. Perhaps a spadeful of translocated soil containing the mycorrhiza could make all the difference.

Other moulds, of which the gardener is only too well aware, are those parasitic ones which attack the tissues of living plants. They send branches of their chain-like cells, or hyphae, in to the host plant and, in their feeding process, damage or destroy their host. It is therefore advisable now to probe a little deeply into the method of growth, reproduction and spread of these plants.

Since there is a close similarity in the behaviour of all the moulds, we can examine one closely and note the divergent details of some of the others. We have already mentioned the condition known as 'damping off' in seedlings and since this is caused by the mould *Pythium* we may as well follow its life story.

If, as it is bound to do since there are plenty floating about in the air, a spore of *Pythium* lands on the soil in which seedlings are growing it will germinate if the conditions (damp soil and a humid atmosphere) are right. Germination involves sending out a hair-like hypha which grows along the soil surface until it comes into contact with the stem of a seedling. Into this it bores, branches and ramifies through the plant tissues, breaking them down and absorbing food from them.

The first visible sign of the presence of *Pythium* in a box of seedlings is when one suddenly falls over. If it be examined it will be seen that the part of the stem just above the soil level is dark-coloured and rotten-looking. The mould now, having acquired strength, will have started sending hyphae out all round and soon will have met and attacked other seedlings.

But this is not their only method of propagation. Some hyphae appear which stand more or less erect, their end becomes swollen and forms a spore. If the conditions are not very damp this spore, when it falls off, simply sends out a hypha as before; but if the conditions are wet, the contents of the spore divide so that a lot of smaller spores, each with a pair of 'tails' are formed. When these are set free by the bursting of the original case, they swim about in the surface dampness till they meet a seedling, bore into it and start its destruction.

If *Pythium* is seen to be active, its ravages can be stopped by getting the seedlings into a dry atmosphere as soon as possible. Most of the moulds and mildews behave in a smilar way, though those which attack leaves of the potato (blight) or roses (mildew) obviously are less dependent on dampness so do not have the actively swimming spores.

Some moulds have a more complicated life-story in that they have to pass one part of their life on one host on which they produce spores. These cannot infect that host, but have to find another. The spores produced on that one then infect the first host. The best-known mould behaving in this way is wheat rust which, in one stage, attacks the wheat plant and in the other stage the barberry. In such a case eradication of the disease is fairly easy since, if all the barberry plants adjacent to wheat lands are destroyed the rust will be destroyed also.

Some moulds in the soil do considerable damage to roots and the one most likely to interest the gardener is *Plasmodiophora brassicae* (usually called 'slime fungi') which attacks and causes the condition known as club-root or finger-and-toe in plants such as cabbages and turnips. Since lime in the soil is a deterrent to the existence of moulds it should always be present where such crops are grown.

The smuts are moulds which live almost completely within the plant, and attack the flower and fruit. They mostly attack the grass family whose fruits become merely black powdery masses of the spores of the mould.

These moulds which cannot be controlled by physical means must be dealt with chemically, and spraying infected leaves with a solution containing copper (copper sulphate and lime being the well-known Bordeaux mixture) or dusting with sulphur is the most effective.

Rotating the crops is of importance in avoiding the attack of moulds because it reduces the chances of re-infection if a crop is grown in ground new to it instead of ground in which it has been grown before.

If a crop becomes infested in this way it is always possible that some few plants will not be attacked. These are said to be resistant to the parasite and if the seed from such plants be collected and later sown it is possible to breed an immune variety from them: immunity behaves as a Mendelian dominant, described earlier. Another method is deliberately to subject a group of plants to a particular parasite and propagate by cuttings those not affected.

If a parasite is carried on the seed it can be controlled by treating or 'dressing' the seed with some chemical substance which will destroy the parasite only. Such a chemical might be mercuric chloride, copper sulphate, formalin or thiram.

Since many of these parasites pass the winter in a resting stage in the dead parts of the plant which they have attacked (haulms of potatoes, etc.) all such material should be burnt, and not kept for compost.

Because of this ability on the part of moulds to remain dormant and because of the small size of their resting spores, they can find comfortable lodgement in the walls of seed-boxes, porous pots, seed-pans and the pieces of broken pots used for drainage. If these are simply put aside and used again without treatment the fresh soil put into them is sure to be infected, to the detriment of the new plants. They should, therefore, be thoroughly sterilised before use.

Cuprinol, a compound containing copper, is the best material for treatment of wooden boxes, which should be soaked with it and allowed to dry. The clay pots and pans should be washed in Cheshunt compound.

Bacteria

Bacteria can, for our purposes, be considered as very small moulds. They mostly consist of a single cell or a chain of cells of no great coherence. They too, form spores which can be carried by wind currents.

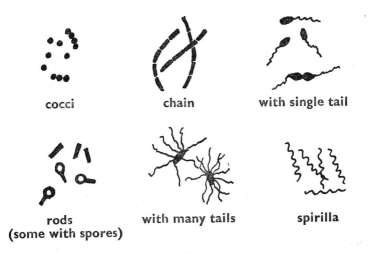

cocci   chain   with single tail

rods
(some with spores)   with many tails   spirilla

FIG. 22. *Some of the different kinds of bacteria.*

When the soil is more alkaline than is suitable for the existence of moulds, it becomes an ideal home for bacteria and they,
in turn, do the same job as did the moulds. Though they are
extremely small (a quarter of a million could lie on the stop at
the end of this sentence!) their vast numbers compensate for
their lack of individual size. Now all living things must have a
means of liberating the energy necessary for their life-processes
and the work they do: our method is to combine the food we eat
with oxygen or in other words, burn it. Thus does a locomotive
liberate energy for movement. In as much as we use the oxygen
of the air we are called aerobic organisms, like dogs and
elephants, all the green plants and lots of bacteria. Some bacteria, however, can break other things down and, in the process,
liberate usable energy and they are therefore called anaerobic
organisms, since they do not use the oxygen of the air. It is this
faculty which allows them to live and work in the centre of a
manure heap and a septic tank where, of course, there is no
oxygen.

Since the harder we work the hotter we get, so does the
temperature rise when bacteria are working. For this reason, a
hot-bed made of unrotted manure generates a considerable
amount of heat; when the rotting is complete the bacterial
activity decreases and with it the temperature.

All living things need a supply of nitrates; we get ours from
the animal and plant matter which we eat; the green plants take
theirs in the form of nitrates in watery solution from the soil;
lots of bacteria do the same, but some have the ability to collect
and 'fix' nitrogen gas from the air. These are the nitrogen-fixing
bacteria whose function is very important because they are
returning to the soil nitrogen which has escaped into the atmosphere where it is no use at all.

Some of the nitrogen-fixers have, so to speak, got on to a good
thing by trading their surplus of nitrates with particular green
plants for a moiety of the surplus sugar they have made. This
form of symbiosis occurs between the leguminous plants and
Rhizobium which enters the roots of the plant. The plant then

forms a case round the bacteria in which the exchange is carried on. (Such nodules can easily be seen on the roots of pea-plants if pulled up and examined when fruiting is past.) As a result of this, such leguminous plants as peas and beans require but little in the way of nitrates in the soil; indeed, if the soil is rich in nitrates the plants will not make use of the bacteria and this is a gross waste to the gardener who has been spending money for something he can get for nothing.

17

NITROGEN CIRCULATION – VIRUSES – THE MUSHROOM – ANTIBIOTICS

Nitrogen Circulation

IN EARLIER CHAPTERS we have talked of putting this and that into the soil, thereby implying that this and that has been taken out of it. In summer the garden was covered with flowers and vegetables but by early spring all are gone. And what has gone represents much that has been taken out of the soil. Now, before another season's crops are grown all that was removed has to go back; if not, we shall get increasingly poorer crops. As there is a cycle of the seasons, so there is a cycle of fertility which embraces all the soil constituents. To discuss such a cycle in detail would be an enormous and somewhat pointless task. But a useful picture can be drawn by considering one important substance, namely, nitrogen. It occurs as such in the atmosphere where it is no use to garden plants however much it comes into contact with them. It has, therefore, to be combined with something which will form a soluble salt. In that state the plant can use it; we use some of what the plant has built up; dead plants, our waste and ourselves go back to the soil and some of our constituents become simple nitrates again, some go off to the air as nitrogen – and so the cycle goes on. Fig. 23 will indicate aspects of the process.

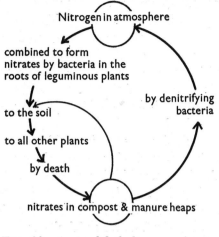

FIG. 23. *A simplified diagram showing the nitrogen cycle.*

Viruses

There was a time when we were young that the concepts of science were beautifully discrete. We learnt that atoms were the smallest particles of matter and further division thereof was impossible: elements were basic substances which always were just that: living things were so clearly divided from non-living things that a child could tell them apart. Nowadays atoms are such gross lumps of matter that one almost expects to see the physicists using them as golf balls: the chemist takes a compound, puts it into his mill, adds a little heavy water, turns the dial to Uranium 999, shakes it with a million volts, and out pops a different element: the biologist is not so certain about his viruses. They are very small indeed, and can only be seen as shadows by the electron microscope. They will pass through a filter made from an unglazed porcelain plate. They will only 'live' in living tissues and some of them at least can be crystallised like sugar and yet revert to the 'living' state. Thus the distinguishing line between what is alive and what is not becomes somewhat blurred. 'Tis indeed an odd age we live in!

Where I here refer to viruses as being in the living state I really mean that they multiply, which indicates that they must feed and grow and reproduce, which no definitely non-living thing does.

Viruses are extremely difficult to study because of their smallness and because they will not reproduce outside a living organism. It is easy to see their effects on plants, and that they are the cause of a particular condition or disease can be shown by introducing the juices of a diseased plant into a normal healthy one. Herein lies a danger in grafting if care is not taken to see that both stock and scion are free from virus infection.

Plant-sucking insects, aphids in particular, are transmitters of virus diseases since they, passing from one plant to another, are very dangerous inoculators. It is a little odd that the plant shoot and its appendages – leaf, flower and fruit – seem to be the main though not the only parts of the plant attacked by viruses. This points still more directly to tissue-piercing insects as the main carriers, though root contamination is possible.

Since plant viruses are transmitted mainly by insects, it is imperative that all possible measures be taken to keep the latter under control, aphids especially.

Since the control of virus disease is so closely linked with the control of aphids it may be worth while looking into the complicated and unusual life-story of these insects.

In spring there hatch from last season's eggs, wingless female insects which make their way to buds and young shoots. There, using their sharp proboscis, they puncture the plant tissues and suck out the juices. Hatching can take place very early in the year, for the same heat which causes buds to open causes the eggs to hatch (I have, on occasion, found the opening buds of honeysuckle suffering from a mild infestation of aphids at the end of January).

The great number of aphids is a direct result of their peculiar method of reproduction. The first lot of insects to hatch out of the eggs are wingless females. These crawl to the soft tissues of the open buds and begin to feed and grow. When fully grown they rapidly produce young which are also wingless females.

Since this process has not involved any sexual act it is said to be parthenogenic. When the second brood of females is two or three days old, they too begin to produce young parthenogenically, and as every new generation does the same, there is little wonder that greenflies are abundant.

Sometimes, especially if the supply of plant juice begins to fall off, a generation of winged females is produced. These fly off and, having settled on other plants, begin to infest them with their offspring.

Towards the end of summer, males, which are winged, are born, and the females fertilized by them lay the eggs which resist the winter's cold.

Though greenflies have many enemies in birds and lady-bird beetles their vast rate of reproduction makes their control difficult, and they can only be checked by the use of sprays containing such substances as derris or nicotine, very soapy water (horticultural 'wetter', not domestic detergent) plus a little paraffin will help in an emergency. These should be applied, of course, when they first appear.

The black or bean aphids tend to spend the winter on and have their first meal off the spindle tree, so it is not advisable to have these plants in or about a garden.

To make matters more difficult there are many kinds of aphid, some confined to one or two plants. For instance the well-known woolly aphid attacks apple trees; adelges are confined to conifers. Others may have a less narrow choice and range over a group of plants.

The Mushroom

The mushroom is a fungus and so a non-green plant. It is therefore unable to make its own supply of food and must live on already prepared organic matter and since it lives on such matter in the dead state, it is a saprophyte.

The mushroom can best be understood by considering the moulds discussed in the last chapter. Spores landing on suitable material, usually soil containing a high proportion of dung, germinate and form hyphae. These run all over the food material, branching and uniting until they form a tangled network called the mycelium.

Some of the uniting hyphae begin to form a knob-like mass just under the soil surface. This grows upwards and begins to differentiate into a stalk and head, but it should be noted that these parts are not composed of cells in any way different from those of the hyphae.

As the umbrella-like top forms, its underside produces downwards a great number of radially placed plates, and from the free ends of the cells forming the plates tiny stalks grow out and the end of each of these gets thickened to form the reproduction spore. Since the spore will germinate and give rise to a new plant the method of reproduction is asexual.

It should be noted that the real 'plant' is the tangle of the mycelium underground and the mushroom we see is merely the reproductive part.

In the growing of mushrooms light is not necessary. so any cellar or outhouse will do for them. But the soil in which they are grown must have a very high organic content. To this end quantities of horse manure are recommended, but with the reduced number of horses such manure is a scarce commodity. However, composted straw treated with animal urea is said to be a good substitute. When the beds are made they are infected with what is called mushroom spawn. This is really a trade term since, speaking accurately, the spores should be called the spawn. However, the spawn is actually compressed blocks or slabs of manure with a great quantity of the mycelium running through it. When broken up and scattered through the bed, the mycelium becomes active again and gives rise to mushrooms.

One of the disadvantages of a bed containing so much organic matter is that it is an ideal site for the growing of other fungi which, in time, may well oust the mushrooms. The soil must therefore be sterilised by heat and absolute cleanliness must be maintained around the bed.

Antibiotics

Seed-producing plants arrange by devious methods to scatter their seed far and wide so that, when they germinate, there will not be too many plants of the same kind living in close competition.

The moulds (and some other lowly plants) indulge in another method of getting living-space. They send out from their hyphae some substance which extends through the matter around them and poisons competitors, leaving themselves a free field.

This was first noticed in the case of cultures of the mould *Penicillium* grown in a laboratory. When the substance excreted from the mould was isolated and extracted it was called penicillin. Since that time it has been found that many, if not all, moulds produce some substance with a similar effect on other moulds and bacteria and these substances have been grouped together under the name of antibiotics. It is possible, therefore, that the destruction of the mushroom mycelia in a highly organic mushroom bed may be due to the antibiotics produced by other moulds. This would seem to be borne out by the fact that heat or chemical sterilisation brings the bed back to normal again, for such moulds are easily destroyed by these treatments.

Soil-sickness is probably also caused by this means. The sickness is a condition not uncommon in well manured soils in which plants will not grow properly. Investigation shows that though there is plenty of nitrogenous matter present it does not break down to the simple soluble nitrates which the plant needs. More careful examination also shows that the numbers of bacteria are too low to deal with the organic matter, while the number of protozoans (single-celled animals) has greatly increased – their numbers being a measure of the sickness, not its cause. If now such sick soils are treated with a poison such as formalin, their condition will improve, thus suggesting that the moulds, less resistant than the bacteria, have been killed. Since they no longer produce the antibiotics which killed the bacteria, the latter increase in numbers, begin breaking down the organic matter and the soil becomes healthy again.

So, among the higher plants we find biological competition, but among the lower ones it is chemical competition. Shall we change a couple of words and call these states biological warfare and chemical warfare and so be almost up-to-date?

Practical Work

1. *Moulds.* Damp a piece of bread, lay it on a saucer and cover it with a sheet of glass. Soon moulds will begin to grow on it. Make a diagram of their position on the bread and note their colour (they will be mostly blue, but if a red patch appears that is a bacterial colony – it is quite harmless). Make daily sketches showing the spread of the various colonies. Note when they begin to form spores (they then look black).

2. *Mushroom spores.* Lay a ripe mushroom or toadstool 'umbrella', gills downwards, on a piece of paper. Leave it for a few days, then lift it and you will see the spores, which have fallen out, arrange to correspond with the position of the gills.

18

NATURAL ORDERS—THE FLORAL DIAGRAM

Natural orders

IT IS OBVIOUS to anyone who cares to look, that all flowers are not of the same shape nor have the same number of parts, and it is by this variation that plants are classified. All those whose flowers are built on the same general plan are said to be in the same Natural Order. The orders are further divided into increasingly smaller groups until we reach Genera and finally Species. Thus the *Rosaceae* contains such genera as *Potentilla* (the cinquefoil group), *Rubus* (raspberry group), *Rosa* (rose group), *Prunus* (plum group), *Crataegus* (hawthorn group) and many more. To none of these can we put a common name because it does not indicate any *specific plant*. When, however, we deal with a specific plant we use the specific name thus, *Potentilla palustris* which stands for the marsh cinquefoil, *Potentilla anserina* is silverweed, *P. sterilis* is the barren strawberry, *Rosa canina* is the wild or dog rose, and so on.

Mention has already been made about the structure of a flower and we must return to the subject in order to understand the classification.

The flowering plants are divided into the two main groups monocotyledons and dicotyledons, the former having their parts in three while the latter have their parts in fours and fives (or some multiple of these), five being the commonest.

The flower is the part of the plant set aside for sexual reproduction by the formation of seed, and is basically constructed as follows: –

The end of the flowering stem is somewhat thickened to form a platform or receptacle on which the flower parts are set in rings or whorls. The lowest of these whorls is composed of sepals (which, taken together, are called the calyx). They are usually green and leaf-like, but they may be coloured and indistinguishable from petals; they may be absent.

The next whorl is composed of the petals (together called the corolla). These are seldom green and leaf-like, but may be white or coloured. They may, like the sepals, be individually distinct so that they can be pulled off separately, or they may be joined together either to a small extent or to form a tube. Sometimes the petals and sepals are so much alike that together they are called the perianth.

Within the corolla there may be one or more whorls of stamens (together the androecium). Each stamen is composed of a thin stalk or filament, at whose top is a thickened part called the anther, in which the pollen is produced. This is the male part of the flower.

Finally, in the middle there is the gynaecium. This is basically composed of a box (the carpel) containing one or more eggs or ovules. The top of the box is drawn into a neck (the style) whose free end (the stigma) produces a sugary substance on which the pollen grains stick. This is the female part of the flower.

As with the other flower parts, there may be considerable deviation from this simple plan, and it is very usual to find that a number of carpels have become joined together to form one box divided into compartments as a multiple ovary. This we may describe as bi-, tri-, tetra-locular, or more simply as two-, three-, or four-celled.

As a result of the fusion of the carpels, the styles and stigmas usually become fused too to form one, though sometimes they retain to some extent their individuality. This composite part is the pistil.

A further complication is introduced by the position of the various whorls in relation to the pistil, and this is due to the shape of the receptacle. If it is a mere thickened continuation of the flower stalk, the whorls will arise one above the other in the way already described, so the ovary will be highest and is then said to be superior. Conversely, the other flower parts will be below the ovary so the flower may be called hypogynous.

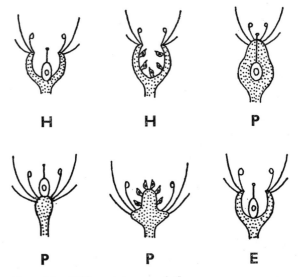

FIG. 24. *Different types of flower arrangements.*
H, hypogynous; P, perigynous; and E, epigynous.

If the receptacle is a mere flat table the ovary will be in the middle, surrounded by the other whorls, so the flower is perigynous. But sometimes the edge of the receptacle is bent up into the form of a cup with the ovaries in the inner side or at the bottom with the other flower parts arising from the lip of the cup, as in the rose. This form is still considered to be perigynous. There is still another possiblity, for sometimes the receptacle, as well as being flat, may be extended upwards in the middle as a

I

knob on which the ovaries are fixed, but this does not alter the fact that the flower is perigynous, while the ovary is, of course, still superior.

If the flower structure is such that the various whorls seem to arise from the top of the ovary, the flower is said to be epigynous and the ovary inferior.

The Floral Diagram

We have, in the foregoing, looked at a flower as if it were cut vertically, but we can also imagine that all the parts are lying in the same horizontal plane and then cut it across. If we do this we get a different picture and one which tells us quite a lot. Such a picture is called a floral diagram.

The floral diagram of a wild rose, for instance, shows that the sepals are joined together but that the petals are not; that the stamens are roughly on radii and not just scattered about; that the carpels are single and do not form a many-celled ovary. The axis of the flower in relation to the stalk is usually indicated by a dot.

We can describe the diagram (and hence the flower) by a simple formula. If we indicate the calyx by K, corolla by C.

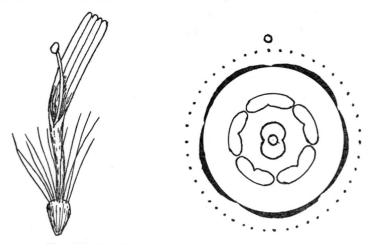

FIG. 25. *The floret and floral diagram of a dandelion.*

androecium by A and gynaecium by G, putting after each the number of the parts and bracketing those that are joined; and further, if by drawing a line over or under the number after G, we indicate whether the ovary is inferior or superior, we have gone a fair way towards telling a lot about the flower. If the petals are coloured like the sepals so that they cannot be distinguished, P to indicate a perianth, is used instead of K and C. Thus the floral formula of the iris, a monocotyledon and member of the *Iridaceae*, is:—

$$\overline{P(3 + 3) \, A3 + \overline{OG(3)}}$$

Let us now consider some of the common Natural Orders into which plants are grouped. There are, however, about a hundred of these in Britain alone so it is not possible here to touch on more than a few of them.

The Natural Orders can be grouped by the process of ever-diminishing groups, following the key by the numbers: –

(1) Monocotyledons. Flower parts in three or multiples of three. – *Amaryllidaceae*, for example, daffodil; *Iridaceae*, for example, iris.

(2) Dicotyledons with both calyx and corolla present, 3. Dicotyledons with one or both absent, 5.

(3) Flower parts in fours. Pistils fused (syncarpous). – *Crucifereae*, for example, wallflower, cabbage, turnip, cress.

Flower parts in fives, 4.

(4) (a) Petals not united: –

Flowers regular: stamens fixed to receptacle, more than 20, pistils separate, hypogynous. – *Ranunculaceae*, for example, buttercup, Christmas rose, marsh marigold.

Stamens fixed to calyx, otherwise as above. – *Rosaceae*, for example, rose, meadow-sweet, apple, pear, raspberry.

Flowers irregular, 10 stamens fixed to calyx. – *Leguminosae*, for example, pea, bean, clover, broom.

(b) Petals united: –

Corolla regular. Ovary inferior. Many florets form-ing a head like one flower, each head surrounded by coloured bracts resembling petals. True petals like scales or hairs. – *Compositae*, for example, dandelion, thistle, daisy, sunflower, lettuce.

Corolla irregular. Ovary superior of two cells, each with many ovules. – *Scrophulariaceae*, for example, a foxglove, antirrhinum, eye-bright, mullein.

Ovary superior of four cells, almost separate and each with one large ovule. – *Labiatae*, for example, deadnettle, mint, thyme, sage.

(5) Calyx present, corolla absent. Herbs with tiny unisexual flowers. – *Urticaceae*, for example, stinging nettle.

Both calyx and corolla absent. Shrubs or trees with catkins. – *Salicaceae*, for example, willow, sallow, poplar.

19

GRASSLANDS – CORNFIELDS – CHALKLANDS – WOODLANDS – MOORLANDS AND BOGS – MARSHES, LAKES AND RIVERS – SEA-SHORE

CERTAIN PLANTS in a garden grow best in particular parts of it. Thus, some prefer full sunshine and well-drained soil; some do best where it is damp; some will only grow in the shade of a tree, and so on.

As one would expect, wild plants arrange themselves in the most suitable habitats and, therefore, since all with special preferences will be found growing together, they are called associations.

Though there are obviously a vast number of such associations, depending on the narrowness of our definition, it is usual for the non-specialist to consider only a few obvious ones. In each of these a fairly permanent and balanced community lives and will continue to do so until something occurs to upset the normal, basic conditions. The draining of a marsh, for instance, by reducing the high water-content of the soil, will very soon see a totally different set of plants colonising its surface.

It is possible so to work out the composition of such an association that, by knowing a few plants growing in a particular place, one is able to make a fair estimate of what the other plants

133

and the nature of the soil will be. Thus, reference to a 'beech-wood association' should instantly produce a mental picture very different from that of an 'oakwood association'.

Grassland Association

The grassland type of plant community has been seen by all, but of those who have walked over it, comparatively few have really looked at it closely. Those who have done so will have noticed that one type of grassland differs from another. The grasses composing a lawn are not the same as those composing a meadow which may be cut for hay, nor is it the same as that found on a hillside.

Grass growing on loams and clays is doing so under the best conditions and becomes a dense mat owing to the great number of plants which the land can support, and also because such land is not growing 'wild' grasses but grasses which have been specially sown as food for stock either by grazing or by hay. This type of grassland would be known as meadow. Besides the grasses in them, meadows also support a considerable flora of dicotyledons which are fairly characteristic.

Where the soil of grassland tends to become waterlogged and sour, the tussock-grasses occur, so that the surface is rough and hummocky.

On gravel soils which are too well drained, the grasses are of the type with thin, hair-like leaves which reduce evaporation and so protect the plant from the effect of excessive drought.

Arable land, especially that growing cereal crops, because of its richness also supports a flora of 'weeds'. Owing to the closeness of the plants of such crops they cannot be hoed like a turnip or potato crop, so unwanted plants may flourish to a larger extent among them.

Plants of the meadows and grassland are bird's foot trefoil, bugle, cat's ear, cowslip, devil's bit scabious, goat's beard, ground ivy, hop trefoil, knapweed, lady's mantle, lady's smock, meadow crane's bill, meadow sweet, marguerite, ragged robin, self-heal.

Plants of the Cornfields

Plants of the cornfields are charlock, corn cockle, corn marigold, corn spurrey, field bugloss, fumitory, heartsease, scarlet pimpernel, soapwort, white campion.

The Chalklands

The great rolling downlands of the southern part of England are composed of hills of chalk covered with a thin layer of soil. Though the chalk itself is a limy or alkaline substance, it does not follow that the soil above it, in which the plants grow, is alkaline, too. Chalk being very porous, rain passing through the soil above will carry down the soluble plant foods as well as what chalk may be in the soil, until it becomes rather poor.

This thin layer of soil is easily dried out, so the plants growing in it are usually rather small in size though abundant in numbers. This latter fact is clearly shown in the summer by the wonderful display of flowers which clothe the downs in a blaze of colour.

If a hole be dug through the soil layer down into the chalk it can be seen that there are two types of plants present, namely, those whose roots are so short that they remain in the soil-layer, and those whose roots are exceedingly long and pass right down into the chalk itself.

Plants of the chalklands are guelder rose, dogwood, spindle tree, wayfaring tree, centaury, stemless thistle, carline thistle, dwarf thistle, round-headed rampion, rock rose, sainfoin, salad burnet, small scabious, wild thyme, yellow-wort, knapweed, wild carrot, hoary plantain, cowslip, milk-wort, bird's foot trefoil, yarrow, mouse-eared hawkweed, various orchids.

The Woodlands

Woodlands are often composed of trees all of the same kind as well as of a mixture of kinds, and since different trees have different effects on the vegetation beneath them we must consider them separately.

The beechwood throws a very dense shade because the trees have a great number of small leaves. Since we have already seen that plants require light in order to grow properly, it is easy to understand why the floor of such a wood is so bare and barren. Add to this the fact that beechwoods are usually found growing on dry chalk soil which has not enough surface moisture to cause the carpet of dead leaves to rot quickly, and so does not offer suitable conditions for the germination of seed.

In dense beechwoods often the only plants to be seen are the rather unpleasant-looking bird's nest and bird's nest orchid. These plants live as saprophytes, so do not require light and do not develop chlorophyll.

Round the edge of the beechwood and its more open spaces a few green plants may occur. These are characteristically sanicale, dog's mercury, bluebell, wood sorrel, primrose, enchanter's nightshade.

The oakwoods occur on soils with little or no lime. The oak shade is not at all dense, so there is an abundance of plants beneath the trees. If the oakwood is on dry ground there is a fairly extensive scrub consisting of brambles, wild roses, holly, ivy and other bushes. Among the herbs we would expect to find foxglove, woodsage, anemone, red campion, tormentil and others.

In wet oakwoods the oaks are bigger, the scrub is more abundant and the herbs occur in greater profusion.

A most interesting point is that the most common oak tree in each of these habitats is of a particular species. In the dry oakwood it is the sessile oak whose leaves have a long stalk but whose acorns are attached directly to their twig; in the wet oakwoods we find the pedunculate oak whose leaves have a short stalk, while the acorns have a long one.

The pinewood: When a pinewood is planted the young trees are set at no great distance apart so, as they grow, their branches intermingle and a dense canopy is formed under which nothing grows. After the first thinning in about ten years' time, a little more light manages to penetrate to the floor, but this again is soon shut off by further growth of the trees which are left. It is only after a long time, when the trees have been thinned again, by felling or storm, that enough light penetrates to allow an undergrowth to develop. When this stage is reached bracken often appears, and with it ling, heather, blaeberry, tormentil and other heath plants.

There are, of course, other forms of woodlands such as ashwoods and birchwoods as well as the woods of mixed composition. If such occur in your neighbourhood it is worth investigating them from the point of view of their tree-composition, amount of shade in the spring and in the summer, the amount of scrub and its composition as well as the herb population.

Moorlands and Bogs

Moorlands may be of various types, but all are characterised by the presence of peat. This substance is really a mass of dead and partially decayed vegetation. It does not decay completely because it is usually wet and forms such a sodden mass that neither earthworms nor bacteria can live in it to break it down. It, therefore, forms a very poor soil, and such plants as grow on it have to be specially adapted to do so. Most of them, for instance, have very small leaves because moorlands are often wind-swept and if the plants had large leaves they would be dried up or torn off. Many have no root-hairs such as are possessed by plants living in ordinary soil.

There is another type of moorland where there is but a thin layer of peat resting on a very porous soil such as gravel. This layer of peat absorbs the rain but does not let much of it pass through. When the rain stops, the water in the peat quickly evaporates from it and it becomes dry once more.

It will be seen that neither of these types of moorland will support many kinds of plants. Both are colonised by ling and heather. While bramble, gorse, broom, larch and birch and various characteristic grasses may be found on the dry heath, the wet heath will support bilberry, bog myrtle, bog asphodel, cotton grass, eyebright, milkwort, tormentil, spotted orchis and the fly-catching plants, butterwort and the round and long-leaved sundews.

It is only a step, so to speak, from the wet moorland to the peat bog in which there is actually standing water. The characteristic plant here is sphagnum moss, but the dark and gloomy waters of the bog may be brightened by the lovely flowers of the water lily and the bog bean.

Marshes, Lakes and Rivers

Where dry land slopes gently to a lake or river we may get three types of habitat in succession. The highest type, be it grassland or woodland, has already been discussed. As the water is approached we may meet land which becomes increasingly wet until, here and there, water may be seen on the surface. This is the marsh proper and may merge into the permanent water of the lake or river.

Along with this change in land condition there will be a change in the type of plants. If we imagine a case which starts with grassland, the normal grassland plants will be replaced as the land gets wetter with such plants as rushes, sedges, marsh marigold, cuckoo flower, forget-me-not, meadow sweet and mare's tail, and all these plants, though they may appear to be growing on land, have their roots in water.

A little further down, where water may be seen on the surface, the characteristic plants are flowering rush, common reed, reed mace, yellow flag, water dropwort, brooklime and perhaps bullrushes at the water's edge.

In the actual water of the lake itself the plants may be growing on the bottom and extending up through the surface of the water, or they may be floating. Since both kinds get a considerable amount of support from the water their stems will be quite soft. The leaves of those growing below the water surface will tend to be long and narrow (as in the *Chara*, milfoil and water violet), or very small and numerous (as in the Canadian pondweed), while those whose leaves float are often broad and flat (water lily, duckweed and broad-leaved pondweed, for example).

In rivers, which, of course, differ from lakes in that the water is moving, the plants have very flexible stems, otherwise they would get broken by the pressure of the moving water.

The Sea-shore

The sea-shore has to be looked upon as the meeting-place of land, sea and air rather than a particular habitat, for in it the conditions vary so much that the plants are subjected to different conditions at different times. It is a place where there is little peace and quiet, for winds and waves may exert forces on the inhabitants such as are never found, for example, in a woodland. This very nature of the shore – its contrasting environments and physical conditions, calm and storm, heat and cold, salt and fresh water – calls from the inhabitants ingenuities in order that they may live.

Shores may be of two main types, the gently shelving sands up and down which the tidal waters may creep or on which mighty rollers may fall with the weight of many tons; or it may be rocky and steep, receiving the force of the wind-driven sea, great enough to heave enormous boulders about. In each type, however, there will be sheltered inlets and coves where plants will flourish.

Sand and shingle offer a poor footing for plants because, below high-water mark, their particles are moving by the water and are likely to destroy any living thing by the grinding action. Where there is greater stability, on for instance, the sheltered rocky or bouldery shore – a survey of the plants can produce interesting results.

Choosing a day and time when the tide is at its lowest, walk *down* the beach from high-water mark to low-water mark and you will find the seaweeds arranged in bands (zones) roughly parallel to the tidal edge.

Zone 1 will be composed of a small, tufty weed called *Pelvetia*.

Zone 2 will be a broad band of *Fucus*, one species of which has floats and is called bladder-wrack, while another species has no floats but the edges of its fronds are toothed, so it is called serrated-wrack.

Zone 3 is exposed only at the lowest spring tides when the oarweed or *Laminaria* becomes visible.

On the dry land above high-water mark, there may be found a fairly characteristic group of flowering plants which are able to withstand the great amount of salty spray to which they may be subjected. They are rock rose, sea scurvy-grass, sea pink and sea scentless mayweed in the rock-cracks; sea purslane, sea beet and common orache in the shingle; and among the sand, sea rocket, sandwort and saltwort.

INDEX

Absciss layer, 49 (Fig. 9)
Africa, 73-4
Agar, 80
Amaryllidaceae, 131
America, 73-4
Androecium, 128, 130
Anemone, 136
Angiosperms, 38
Antirrhinum, 132
Aphids, 122-3
Apple, 54, 58, 61, 67, 88-9, 101, 123, 131
Arbrex, 93
Ashwoods, 137
Asplenium bulbiferum, 109
Australia, 73
Auxins, 89

Bacteria, kinds of, 117 (Fig. 22)
Barberry, 72, 115
Bark-ringing, 95 (Fig. 17)
Bateson, William, 101
Beans, 62, 67, 131
Beech, 136
Bees, 59-60
Beet, 91
Begonias, 37
Bilberry, 137
Birch, 137
Bird's foot trefoil, 134-5
Bird's nest orchid, *see Neottia*
Blackberries, 94
Black currants, 93
Bladder-wort, *see Utricularia*
Bladder-wrack, 139
Blaeberry, 137
Bluebell, 136
Bog asphodel, 137
   bean, 138
   myrtle, 137
Bracken, 137
Bramble, 136-7
Broad beans, 62, 67
Brooklime, 138
Broom, 87, 131, 137

Brunn Abbey, 97-8, 101
Bugle, 134
Burbank, Luther, 101-2
Butcher's broom, 45, 54
Buttercup, 57, 65, 67, 131
Butterworth fly-catchers, 75

Cabbage family, 24, 44, 116, 131
Cacti, 73-4, 101
Calyx, 128, 130-2
Cambial cells, 40
Cambium, 35, 38, 40-1, 44, 84
Campion, red, 136
   white, 135
Capitulum, 67
Carboniferous era, trees of, 106 (Fig. 20)
Carotene, 48
Carpels, 56, 65, 128, 130
Carrot, 63
   effect of soil on, 16 (Fig. 3), 24
   fly, 26
   wild, 67, 135
Cat's ear, 134
Cauliflower, 21
Celandine, lesser, 64
Celery, 48
Cell division, 100 (Fig. 19)
Centaury, 135
Centipedes, 31
Cereals, 134
Chamaecereus silvestrii, 74
Chara, 138
Charlock, 64, 135
Cherries, 58, 101
China, 107
Christmas rose, 131
Chrysanthemum, 91-2
Cinquefoil, 127
Clay, 15, 21
Click-beetle, 30
Clover, 131
Club root, 116
Coal, trees which formed, 106 (Fig. 20)
Cockchafers, 30

141